BLOCKBUSTERS QUIZ BOOK 1

This book adaptation of *Blockbusters*, the very successful Central television series game, can be used in one of two ways. By yourself you can solve the clues as you would a crossword puzzle, writing the answers in the spaces provided and shading or colouring in the hexagons; or, you can play it as a game with friends, one being the quizmaster and two being competitors, one trying to get a linking pattern of hexagons across and one down.

Whether you solve the clues yourself, or with friends, you'll have hours of amusement and have masses of information at your fingertips.

Blockbusters
Quiz Book 1

Based on the Central Independent Television series
produced in association with Mark Goodson and
Talbot Television Ltd

SPHERE BOOKS LIMITED

First published in Great Britain
by Sphere Books Ltd 1985
27 Wrights Lane, London W8 5TZ
Copyright © 1985 by Sphere Books Ltd
Central logo copyright © 1982
Central Independent Television plc.
Central Television programmes © 1983, 1984, 1985
Central Independent Television plc.
Reprinted 1985 (five times), 1986 (six times), 1987

TRADE
MARK

Set in Times

Printed and bound in Great Britain by
Cox & Wyman Ltd, Reading

Blockbusters Quiz
Book 1

M —————————————————   L —————————————————

O —————————————————   S —————————————————

K —————————————————   T —————————————————

D —————————————————   R —————————————————

J —————————————————   C —————————————————

P —————————————————   E —————————————————

H —————————————————   A —————————————————

W —————————————————   V —————————————————

F —————————————————   G —————————————————

B —————————————————   N —————————————————

M: What 'M' is an insect of the order of Lepidoptera?

O: What 'O' is a house containing a hop drying kiln?

K: What 'K' is South Africa's most famous diamond mine?

D: What 'D' in the morse code go with dots?

J: What 'J' comes before Dory, Bull and O'Groats?

P: What 'P' is a document demanding action which is signed by a lot of people?

H: What 'H' was the woman over whose abduction the Trojan War was fought?

W: What 'W' has its greatest density at four degrees centigrade?

F: What 'F' is the pretty thing called 'immortelle'?

B: What 'B' is a drink made from malt and hops?

L: What 'L' is a small rock avalanche, or a huge majority in an election?

S: What 'S' was a king of Israel who was famous for his wisdom?

T: What 'T' goes before deck, measure and recorder?

R: What 'R' is the name for the Mediterranean coast from La Spezia to Hyères?

C: What 'C' is the war that included the battles of Alma and Balaclava?

E: What 'E' is a Christian church festival celebrated on January 6th?

A: What 'A' is a putrid egg?

V: What 'V' are thiamine, niacin, and riboflavin?

G: What 'G' is a comedian's stock-in-trade or something to stop you speaking?

N: What 'N' was a French marshal who was called 'The Bravest of the Brave'?

C _____

I _____

N _____

O _____

F _____

K _____

A _____

P _____

D _____

J _____

B _____

Q _____

H _____

L _____

S _____

R _____

E _____

M _____

T _____

U _____

C: What 'C' is connected with gambling and potatoes?

I: What 'I' means to transfix or stick a spike through?

N: What 'N' is the Himalayan country which is the home of the Gurkhas?

O: What 'O' is a black woodwind instrument with a double reed?

F: What 'F' do you cross in the House of Commons if you change party?

K: What 'K' is kept in place by an Obi in Japan?

A: What 'A' is what Edward VIII did?

P: What 'P' is a comic strip created by Charles Schultz?

D: What 'D' did England expect every man to do at Trafalgar?

J: What 'J' were in exile in Babylon in the 6th century B.C.?

B: What 'B' is a stimulating drink for invalids, and called tea?

Q: What 'Q' can't you get into a pint pot?

H: What 'H' is a Japanese method of committing suicide?

L: What 'L' can happen to a ship or help you with your shopping?

S: What 'S' is a thing that a ruminant essentially has more than one of?

R: What 'R' is the light at the back of a vehicle that is red, to warn other vehicles coming from behind?

E: What 'E' were the first people to make and wear parkas?

M: What 'M' is the best known Italian soup over here?

T: What 'T' is a fly that is feared in Africa because it transmits sleeping sickness?

U: What 'U' is the two dots placed over a letter in German?

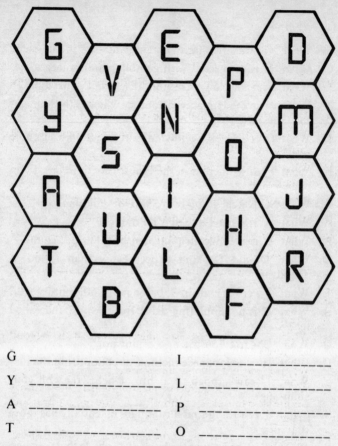

G _____

Y _____

A _____

T _____

V _____

S _____

U _____

B _____

E _____

N _____

I _____

L _____

P _____

O _____

H _____

F _____

D _____

M _____

J _____

R _____

G: What 'G' was the pure knight who sat in the siege perilous?

Y: What 'Y' is a system of Hindu Philosophy having many forms?

A: What 'A' forms the diet of the pangolin and the echidna?

T: What 'T' is an electric lamp filled with batteries, that you carry around with you?

V: What 'V' are stoats, weasels and magpies to a gamekeeper?

S: What 'S' goes before iron, roller and engine?

U: What 'U' are the mammary glands of a goat?

B: What 'B' are nomadic Arabs, who keep horses, cattle and sheep?

E: What 'E' was hurled into a lake at the death of King Arthur?

N: What 'N' when speaking of temperature is the equivalent of zero?

I: What 'I' is the time so ancient that it is beyond memories?

L: What 'L' cannot change its spots?

P: What 'P' was the name given to English 19th century colonists who grew rubber, tea, cotton, coffee and sugar?

O: What 'O' is used to mean the start of a war, of a disease, or of violence?

H: What 'H' is a twenty-fourth part of a mean solar day?

F: What 'F' forms a bird's plumage?

D: What 'D' is any flower that has many sets of petals?

M: What 'M' is the longest running race in the Olympics?

J: What 'J' means to poke roughly, or is slang for an injection?

R: What 'R' is the sort of deal that is harsh or unfair?

C	_____	F	_____
E	_____	T	_____
I	_____	S	_____
N	_____	Y	_____
R	_____	L	_____
W	_____	G	_____
D	_____	P	_____
K	_____	U	_____
B	_____	J	_____
V	_____	A	_____

C: What 'C' is the city associated with Godiva?

E: What 'E' are big and little conrods in a car engine?

I: What 'I' was the major movement in French Art named after a Monet painting?

N: What 'N' is the region of France famous for its beaches and its cheeses?

R: What 'R' has a scut and is kept in a hutch?

W: What 'W' is 'under the bridge' when it is past history?

D: What 'D' is an aimless scrawling, done while thinking about something else?

K: What 'K' is the Himalayan peak thought to be the third highest in the world?

B: What 'B' comes before bottle, bell and blood?

V: What 'V' is a, usually, rambling performance on the organ while a church fills or empties?

F: What 'F' are you sitting on when you shilly shally?

T: What 'T' was the alliance of miners, railwaymen and transport workers in 1913?

S: What 'S' goes before block, price and stalls?

Y: What 'Y' is a root called the sweet potato?

L: What 'L' is a baby hare?

G: What 'G' is a glove thrown down, taken up, or used when driving a car or fencing?

P: What 'P' is a horizontal bar for a cage bird to sit on?

U: What 'U' is a province in Central Italy, which may have given its name to a brown pigment?

J: What 'J' is the southernmost of the Channel Islands?

A: What 'A' is the collective name given to the twelve disciples chosen by Jesus?

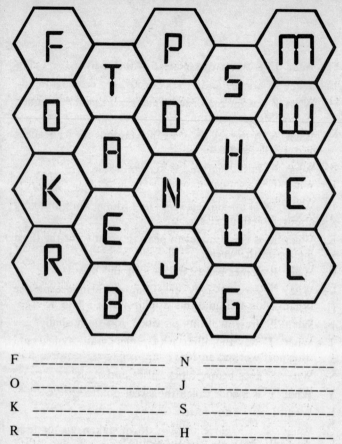

F _____   N _____

O _____   J _____

K _____   S _____

R _____   H _____

T _____   U _____

A _____   G _____

E _____   M _____

B _____   W _____

P _____   C _____

D _____   L _____

5

F: What 'F' is a town in Wales, or a stone used to make sparks?

O: What 'O' is a horse at very long odds, thought unlikely to be placed?

K: What 'K' was a South African called 'Oom Paul' who gave his name to a coin?

R: What 'R' is an inclined beam supporting a roof?

T: What 'T' is a valuable food-fish that has varieties called blue-fin, big-eye, and skipjack?

A: What 'A' is an exciting, dangerous or unusual undertaking, and sometimes goes before playground?

E: What 'E' is what the French want when they shout 'Bis'?

B: What 'B' comes before death, pool and sea?

P: What 'P' is a dealer in ducks, hens, geese and turkeys?

D: What 'D' is the adjective applied to the Middle Ages between the 5th and 8th centuries?

N: What 'N' is the 'N' of DNA and RNA?

J: What 'J' is the adjective applied to furniture and buildings of the early 17th century?

S: What 'S' is a greyish-green herb used for stuffing duck, or used to describe a wise man?

H: What 'H' are both parents of a leveret?

U: What 'U' was an excavated town in Chaldea? (pronounced Kaldea)

G: What 'G' is the Milky Way?

M: What 'M' is a significant line through Greenwich?

W: What 'W' is most likely to be produced in a distillery in Scotland?

C: What 'C' was a German Princess who married, and then succeeded Peter III of Russia?

L: What 'L' is the molten rock forced out of a volcano vent?

M _____

O _____

K _____

D _____

J _____

P _____

H _____

W _____

F _____

B _____

L _____

S _____

T _____

R _____

C _____

E _____

A _____

V _____

G _____

N _____

M: What 'M' comes before pole, flower and fly?

O: What 'O' is where the French Fleet was sunk in 1940?

K: What 'K' is the name given to the pool in some gambling card games?

D: What 'D' is the professional played by Martin Shaw?

J: What 'J' is the central column in an aeroplane cock-pit that controls the elevators and ailerons?

P: What 'P' is a black and white swimming bird that never flies?

H: What 'H' is a point at which the fire brigade can connect to water?

W: What 'W' is a sea mammal that used to provide the so-called 'bones' for women's corsets?

F: What 'F' do you have in the pie when officiously concerned in something?

B: What 'B' are people of the West Pyrenees who are separatists?

L: What 'L' are the short poems that begin: 'There was an old man of Peru...'?

S: What 'S' is an English county which includes Exmoor, and the Cathedral city of Wells?

T: What 'T' is the American word for a dinner-jacket?

R: What 'R' is the slang that makes 'Apples and Pears' into 'stairs'?

C: What 'C' is a person not in one of the armed services?

E: What 'E' precedes Degas, Wallace and Allan Poe?

A: What 'A' is the river that runs through the town where Shakespeare was born?

V: What 'V' came into being between 1943 and 1952 and is called Paricutin?

G: What 'G' is an attic and where poets are supposed to live?

N: What 'N' is to conduct, manage or steer a ship or aircraft?

C _____ B _____

I _____ Q _____

N _____ H _____

O _____ L _____

F _____ S _____

K _____ R _____

A _____ E _____

P _____ M _____

D _____ T _____

J _____ U _____

C: What 'C' are the dried flower buds of a type of myrtle, whose oil is suggested to relieve toothache?

I: What 'I' is dentine, especially when it's an elephant's tusks?

N: What 'N' is one less than ten?

O: What 'O' does a woman sometimes promise she will do when she gets married?

F: What 'F' is the state that includes Palm Beach?

K: What 'K' may a cat look at?

A: What 'A' is the female steward on a plane, called a hostess?

P: What 'P' revolted in England in 1381?

D: What 'D' was the great reception given to George V in Delhi?

J: What 'J' is an iota, whit, or tittle – anyway, something very small?

B: What 'B' is the character in 'Crossroads', played by Paul Henry?

Q: What 'Q' is a landing place, or wharf, for loading and unloading?

H: What 'H' is the official report of proceedings in Parliament?

L: What 'L' is the nearly round green fruit from citrus medica?

S: What 'S' precedes father, mother and ladder?

R: What 'R' is the fruit of the vine when it has been dried?

E: What 'E' is a unit of energy?

M: What 'M' is a bishop's headdress, and often the name of a pub?

T: What 'T' is a stiffened skirt worn by ballerinas?

U: What 'U' is the 'Sinister' supporter of the Royal Arms?

G   _____   I   _____

Y   _____   L   _____

A   _____   P   _____

T   _____   O   _____

V   _____   H   _____

S   _____   F   _____

U   _____   D   _____

B   _____   M   _____

E   _____   J   _____

N   _____   R   _____

G: What 'G' was a gallows where executed criminals were hung?

Y: What 'Y' goes before Mr Lear's Bonghy Bo?

A: What 'A' is an intimate mixture of two or more metals?

T: What 'T' goes before boy, foolery and Tom?

V: What 'V' is a large tub or other vessel for brewing and dyeing?

S: What 'S' comes after mill, gem and cherry?

U: What 'U' is a person who arranges funerals?

B: What 'B' is often oak, and is produced by the sun?

E: What 'E' is a long involuntary absence like that of the Jews in Babylon?

N: What 'N' is the most populous nation in Africa?

I: What 'I' is the order in classic architecture that has scrolled ends to the volutes on its columns?

L: What 'L' is where Theseus slew the Minotaur?

P: What 'P' was the family who wore broom in their hats, that was founded by Geoffrey of Anjou?

O: What 'O' goes before head, hear and heat?

H: What 'H' is the great port on the Humber Estuary which is really called Kingston?

F: What 'F' is the source of linen and linseed oil?

D: What 'D' was the kind of man played by Patrick McGoohan when he was 'John Drake'?

M: What 'M' was the sister of Lazarus and Mary?

J: What 'J' comes before frost, daw and boot?

R: What 'R' is every action said to have?

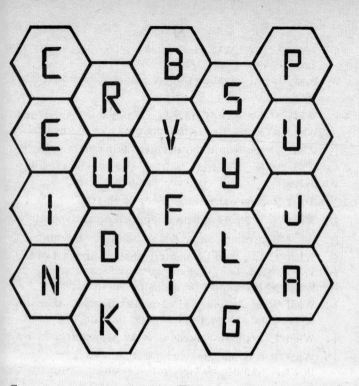

C _____ F _____
E _____ T _____
I _____ S _____
N _____ Y _____
R _____ L _____
W _____ G _____
D _____ P _____
K _____ U _____
B _____ J _____
V _____ A _____

C: What 'C' are Encke's seen in 1818, Biela's seen in 1826, and Donsti's seen in 1858?

E: What 'E' was the ancient, and now poetic, name for Ireland?

I: What 'I' is a way of travelling with name, clothes and character concealed – often resorted to – by royalty?

N: What 'N' became the first Prime Minister of independent India in 1947?

R: What 'R' in South Africa is worth 100 cents?

W: What 'W' is a slender, tightly-corseted waist?

D: What 'D' are thought to have worshipped something at Stonehenge?

K: What 'K' are sheetbands and timber hitches?

B: What 'B' was the profession of Joey Maxim and Floyd Patterson?

V: What 'V' is the Russian river which is the longest in Europe and has singing boatmen?

F: What 'F' disposes of stolen property, or keeps cows in a field?

T: What 'T' is an American golfer known as 'Supermex' or Lee?

S: What 'S' was a city in South Vietnam now called Ho Chi Minh City?

Y: What 'Y' was part of a sailing ship's rigging from which men were hung?

L: What 'L' comes before sentence, class and belt?

G: What 'G' is a kind of bread, beer, ale or snap?

P: What 'P' is a person who makes scent?

U: What 'U' is the name of a large citrus fruit produced by crossing grapefruit and tangerines?

J: What 'J' was Ahab's wife a shameless painted woman who came to a bad end?

A: What 'A' was the vessel into which the animals went two by two?

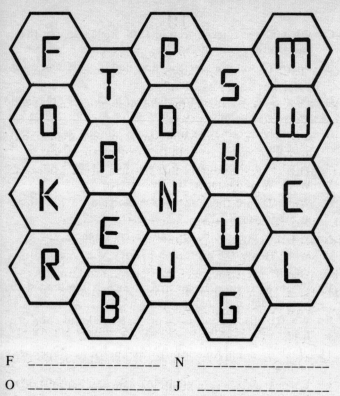

F _____   N _____

O _____   J _____

K _____   S _____

R _____   H _____

T _____   U _____

A _____   G _____

E _____   M _____

B _____   W _____

P _____   C _____

D _____   L _____

F: What 'F' is the biggest bone in the leg?

O: What 'O' is the decision of a cricket umpire when a batsman is dismissed LBW?

K: What 'K' is a place on the Yukon, famous since 1896, when gold was found there?

R: What 'R' is a river rising in Southern Switzerland, and flowing through France to the Mediterranean sea?

T: What 'T' is the country that has had Prime Ministers called Ulusa and Ozal?

A: What 'A' is the 'A' of 'A'-level?

E: What 'E' is a newspaper published after mid-day?

B: What 'B' is a straw hat, with a flat crown and brim, often seen at Henley?

P: What 'P' is the source of the starch called farina?

D: What 'D' goes before off, time and of wrath?

N: What 'N' is a lump of gold?

J: What 'J' is a crowbar (or something similar), carried by a burglar?

S: What 'S' is a backless seat used by a piano player?

H: What 'H' is the epithet applied to a parliament that lacks an effective majority?

U: What 'U' is the opposite of rural and means of the town?

G: What 'G' was stored in the Parthenon by the Turks in 1687 and resulted in its partial destruction?

M: What 'M' is what Michael Jackson does when he appears to walk forward but actually moves backwards?

W: What 'W' was the place where Alice had her first adventures?

C: What 'C' is the force that tends to fly from the centre?

L: What 'L' in Wales was the model for Llareggub and the home of Dylan Thomas?

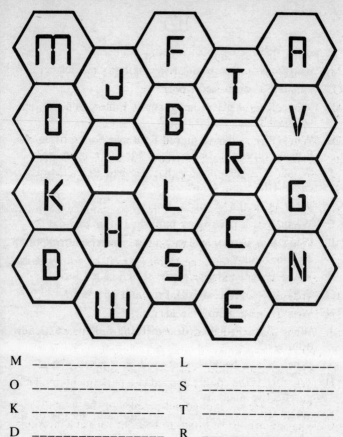

M _____ L _____

O _____ S _____

K _____ T _____

D _____ R _____

J _____ C _____

P _____ E _____

H _____ A _____

W _____ V _____

F _____ G _____

B _____ N _____

M: What 'M' is a flacon and King Arthur's magician?

O: What 'O' is the basis of porridge?

K: What 'K' wrote 'The Knight that Failed' and barrack room ballads?

D: What 'D' is a woman played by a man in pantomine?

J: What 'J' traded the family cow for a sack of beans?

P: What 'P' were the spectacular birds that pulled Juno's chariot?

H: What 'H' can be a horse's joint, a white wine or a pawnshop?

W: What 'W' goes before base, chair and barrow?

F: What 'F' are among the favourite prey of grass-snakes and were once tadpoles?

B: What 'B' is a tree, cove and a window?

L: What 'L' is an item in an auction?

S: What 'S' was the Royal House of Bonnie Prince Charlie?

T: What 'T' is a slight squabble?

R: What 'R' do you do, when wearing jodhpurs?

C: What 'C' is an artificer in wood?

E: What 'E' are the mongoloid peoples of the Arctic?

A: What 'A' is a list of things to be dealt with at a meeting?

V: What 'V' were made by Amati, Guarneri, and Stradivari?

G: What 'G' tells the story of the creation in the Bible?

N: What 'N' is the rossignol famous for singing after dark?

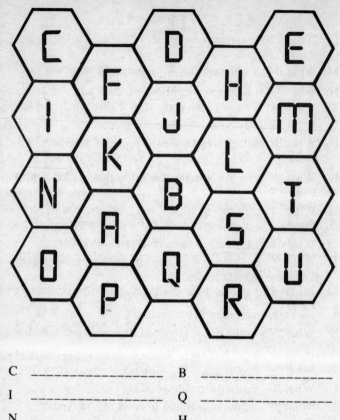

C _____   B _____

I _____   Q _____

N _____   H _____

O _____   L _____

F _____   S _____

K _____   R _____

A _____   E _____

P _____   M _____

D _____   T _____

J _____   U _____

C: What 'C' are the artificial bends introduced into a motor racing course?

I: What 'I' is a device for burning garden or other rubbish?

N: What 'N' has the name Milhouse and was ruined by Watergate?

O: What 'O' is a red or yellow earth pigment?

F: What 'F' is the part of a view, or picture, nearest to the viewer?

K: What 'K' was the surname of the Baptist minister who won the Nobel Peace Prize in 1964 for non-violent resistance to racial inequality?

A: What 'A' is a person who is chronically unable to stop drinking beer, wine or spirits?

P: What 'P' is the largest voracious predatory fish of English fresh water?

D: What 'D' is the adjective applied to wines that aren't sweet?

J: What 'J' is a general feeling of disorientation and fatigue, as a result of long flights?

B: What 'B' with a peculiar pronunciation is the castle of the Duke of Rutland?

Q: What 'Q' means to flinch or cower away, but is also a little game bird?

H: What 'H' is the red pigment of the blood?

L: What 'L' is the text of an opera?

S: What 'S' is a sign that indicates that a note is raised in pitch?

R: What 'R' is the 'R' of 'R & B'?

E: What 'E' is an Australian tree known as a coolabah?

M: What 'M' was slain by Theseus in a labyrinth?

T: What 'T' is the Japanese city that the Shoguns called Edo?

U: What 'U' means customary or occurring in ordinary circumstances?

G _____   I _____

Y _____   L _____

A _____   P _____

T _____   O _____

V _____   H _____

S _____   F _____

U _____   D _____

B _____   M _____

E _____   J _____

N _____   R _____

G: What 'G' was one of England's greatest 18th century portrait painters?

Y: What 'Y' goes before gods and merry gentlemen?

A: What 'A' is the Lord's or the communion table?

T: What 'T' is a large waterproof cloth for covering a ship's hatches or a lorry's load?

V: What 'V' goes with vigour, and cleans the bath?

S: What 'S' comes before tactics, troops, and absorbers?

U: What 'U' is a state within a state which includes Little Russia?

B: What 'B' is the country whose civil aircraft marking is 0 0?

E: What 'E' is the department of public service that looks after the nation's money?

N: What 'N' can be aquiline, pug or snub?

I: What 'I' is a US automobile track race called the 'Five Hundred'?

L: What 'L' was a son of Jacob and is a maker of jeans?

P: What 'P' is a covering for a bed made of lots of little pieces of different material sewn together?

O: What 'O' results in 'no rooms' and is the curse of package tour hotels?

H: What 'H' is food for horses in the form of dried grass?

F: What 'F' do you snap at an authority which you defy?

D: What 'D' is a pop singer and the home town of the 'Dynasty' series?

M: What 'M' founded the Moslem religion?

J: What 'J' is the name given to people who climb chimneys and steeples?

R: What 'R' can be described as pigeon's blood or cabocho and is a gemstone?

C _____
E _____
I _____
N _____
R _____
W _____
D _____
K _____
B _____
V _____

F _____
T _____
S _____
Y _____
L _____
G _____
P _____
U _____
J _____
A _____

14

C: What 'C' is what parents do at babies, and pigeons do in general?

E: What 'E' comes from the Greek for heathen, and is now applied to racial minorities?

I: What 'I' is glowing with heat, like the filament of an electric light bulb?

N: What 'N' is the man who drew far-reaching conclusions from the drop of an apple?

R: What 'R' is a sudden invasion by police to discover violations of the law?

W: What 'W' is it easy to be after the event?

D: What 'D' were the two Type 42 vessels 'Sheffield' and 'Coventry' sunk in the Falklands?

K: What 'K' is another name for the absolute zero temperature scale?

B: What 'B' is the spa where the 1984 SDP Conference was held?

V: What 'V' is a solemn undertaking or promise?

F: What 'F' was the name given to members of the 19th century league for promoting revolution and the end of British rule in Ireland?

T: What 'T' is what you do in order to make a rope into a half hitch?

S: What 'S' is a hot steam bath followed by a cold plunge, that comes from Finland?

Y: What 'Y' is a verb meaning to jerk or pull violently?

L: What 'L' is the Irish river that is an important element in the writings of James Joyce?

G: What 'G' is a Sanskrit word meaning venerable, now used for any spiritual teacher?

P: What 'P' comes exclusively from Douro and is a wine?

U: What 'U' was the English word for a wide range of Hindus of low caste?

J: What 'J' is the very short time preceded by the phrases 'I shan't be a...', and 'it won't take a...'?

A: What 'A' can be Chinese, globe or Jerusalem?

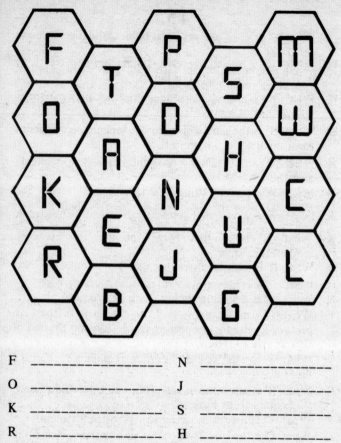

F	_____	N	_____
O	_____	J	_____
K	_____	S	_____
R	_____	H	_____
T	_____	U	_____
A	_____	G	_____
E	_____	M	_____
B	_____	W	_____
P	_____	C	_____
D	_____	L	_____

F: What 'F' is a tall, tapering champagne glass, or a member of the woodwind family?

O: What 'O' is sometimes one-sixteenth, and sometimes one-twelfth of a pound?

K: What 'K' is the part of England where the first Borstal was founded?

R: What 'R' is a small, tasty, red fruit, or a rude noise made with the lips?

T: What 'T' is called a 'tin fish' by the Navy?

A: What 'A' is a chemical substance, often ethylene glycol, added to the water in a car's radiator in the winter?

E: What 'E' was made out of Adam's rib?

B: What 'B' is another name for lotto?

P: What 'P' is a mustard pickle of mixed vegetables?

D: What 'D' can be earth-fill, concrete-arch, or masonry-gravity?

N: What 'N' is a small bunch of fragrant flowers?

J: What 'J' comes before tar, and after steeple?

S: What 'S' sang 'Baby Love'?

H: What 'H' is grated to make a hot sauce for roast beef?

U: What 'U' was once conquered by Poland and is now one of the Soviet Union's chief grain-producing areas?

G: What 'G' is the valley where the MacDonalds were massacred?

M: What 'M' is the army officer below a lieutenant colonel and above a captain?

W: What 'W' is carried by an aqueduct?

C: What 'C' is the famous father of William Arthur Philip Louis?

L: What 'L' is a bloodsucking parasite, once much used by physicians?

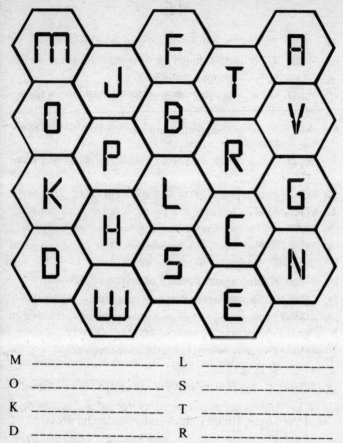

M _____   L _____

O _____   S _____

K _____   T _____

D _____   R _____

J _____   C _____

P _____   E _____

H _____   A _____

W _____   V _____

F _____   G _____

B _____   N _____

M: What 'M' comes before gas, marigold and mallow?

O: What 'O' is used to propel a rowing boat?

K: What 'K' in anatomy is the patella?

D: What 'D' was the title used by Mussolini when a fascist dictator?

J: What 'J' is an acquisitive member of the crow family with a grey head and neck?

P: What 'P' is a red flower of the countryside worn on Remembrance Day?

H: What 'H' was called Hans and was Court painter to Henry VIII?

W: What 'W' means feeble and is often applied to knees?

F: What 'F' was the French Republic that was established in 1946?

B: What 'B' is a shrub and a female singer?

L: What 'L' comes in the form of kid, suede, or pigskin?

S: What 'S' was a boxed-in chair that was carried about in the 18th century?

T: What 'T' was the House that followed York on the English throne?

R: What 'R' are the bones that can be asternal, floating or false?

C: What 'C' is the Indian city famous for a disaster called the Black Hole?

E: What 'E' precedes island, parade, bonnet and Sunday?

A: What 'A' took a thorn out of a lion's foot?

V: What 'V' is a little puff-pastry case filled with meat, or fish and sauce?

G: What 'G' is a thick drink or a thin food made with oatmeal?

N: What 'N' is an actress who was in 'Crossroads' whose name is Gordon?

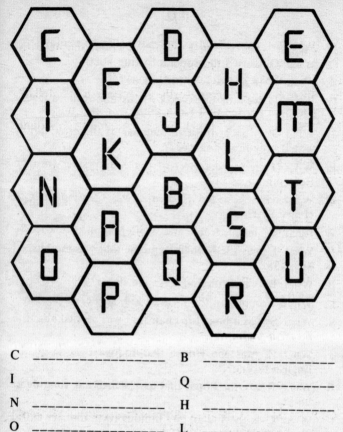

C	_____	B	_____
I	_____	Q	_____
N	_____	H	_____
O	_____	L	_____
F	_____	S	_____
K	_____	R	_____
A	_____	E	_____
P	_____	M	_____
D	_____	T	_____
J	_____	U	_____

C: What 'C' was the first animal to communicate with humans by sign language?

I: What 'I' has a desert called the Negev?

N: What 'N' is a US coin worth one-twentieth of a dollar?

O: What 'O' is white that has a grubby or grey tinge?

F: What 'F' is the bench where the most important members of the Government and Opposition sit?

K: What 'K' is the home of bourbon whiskey?

A: What 'A' is a thing done, a segment of a play or opera, or to perform on the stage?

P: What 'P' is bounded by the Gran Chaco in the north and Patagonia in the south, and is the great plain of Argentina?

D: What 'D' was the birthplace of Yeats, Wilde and Shaw, in Ireland?

J: What 'J' is the large Indonesian island in which fossils of homo erectus were found?

B: What 'B' is normally England's largest cereal crop?

Q: What 'Q' are the misgivings, doubts, or scruples of conscience?

H: What 'H' fell in love with a beautiful Esmeralda at Notre Dame cathedral?

L: What 'L' are the words of a pop song or a song in a musical?

S: What 'S' is the Japanese faith that teaches that the gods live in mountains, rivers and trees?

R: What 'R' is a track for trains?

E: What 'E' was Adlai Stevenson's middle name, or is J R's surname?

M: What 'M' did Eric Liddell become, professionally, after he gave up athletics?

T: What 'T' is a vari-coloured design for woollen cloth, closely associated with the Clans of Scotland?

U: What 'U' is blue-grey clothing worn by people in the airforce?

G _____   I _____

Y _____   L _____

A _____   P _____

T _____   O _____

V _____   H _____

S _____   F _____

U _____   D _____

B _____   M _____

E _____   J _____

N _____   R _____

G: What 'G' is your food pipe or oesophagus?

Y: What 'Y' is an Arab Republic to the South of Saudi Arabia?

A: What 'A' is a pathological loss of appetite often seen in teenage girls?

T: What 'T' is a small stream flowing into a river?

V: What 'V' is a salvo, or a shower of missiles, or a sequence of shots in tennis?

S: What 'S' goes before charmer, bite and skin?

U: What 'U' is a bone in the forearm?

B: What 'B' is the city where the US Embassy was destroyed by a bomb in April 1983?

E: What 'E' is what Schliemann did at Troy, and Carter did in Egypt?

N: What 'N' is Prince William to Princess Anne?

I: What 'I' means to burst inwards and is sometimes applied to stars?

L: In the RAF, what 'L' is the 'L' of 'LAC'?

P: What 'P' is a game show where ten celebrities help Lennie Bennett?

O: What 'O' is successfully to offer more money than someone else at an auction?

H: What 'H' is the part of Scotland known as the Western Isles?

F: What 'F' is a small slit trench for one soldier in battle?

D: What 'D' became Lord Beaconsfield and died in 1881?

M: What 'M' was relieved after a long siege in the Boer War?

J: What 'J' was the Christian name of Charlotte Brontë's most famous character?

R: What 'R' is your backside, or means to bring up to maturity?

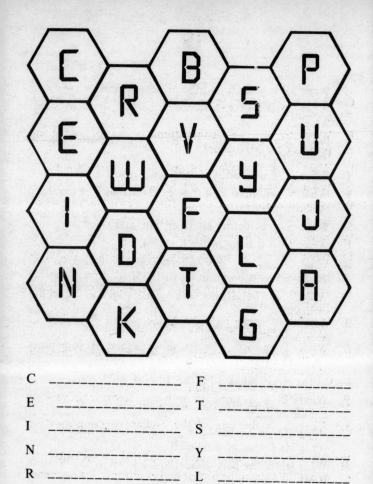

C _____   F _____

E _____   T _____

E _____   S _____

I _____   Y _____

N _____   L _____

R _____   G _____

W _____   P _____

D _____   U _____

K _____   J _____

B _____   A _____

V _____

C: What 'C' is a prize given to someone who hasn't won a contest?

E: What 'E' are the conventional rules of social or professional behaviour?

I: What 'I' can be called red, west or South American?

N: What 'N' was a bushranger Kelly's first name?

R: What 'R' is the sort of punch that is a blow on the back of the neck?

W: What 'W' is a bet or stake?

D: What 'D' had a bump with Miss Budd at the 1984 Olympics?

K: What 'K' was an American but said, 'Ich bin ein Berliner' when he visited Germany?

B: What 'B' was the girl whose lock of hair was seized in Alexander Pope's poem?

V: What 'V' is a document needed for travel through certain countries?

F: What 'F' is an inundation?

T: What 'T' comes from an ore called cassiterite?

S: What 'S' is the sign of the Zodiac covering most of December?

Y: What 'Y' is the wild and domesticated ox of Tibet?

L: What 'L' is the mineral that makes ultramarine pigment?

G: What 'G' was the Nazi secret police?

P: What 'P' is a harbour-town with a customs office?

U: What 'U' describes clothes, or hairdressing, designed to be suitable for men or women?

J: What 'J' is the American slang for W.C., and is a man's name?

A: What 'A' follows crab, love and toffee?

F _____   N _____

O _____   J _____

K _____   S _____

R _____   H _____

T _____   U _____

A _____   G _____

E _____   M _____

B _____   W _____

P _____   C _____

D _____   L _____

F: What 'F' is the spin you get into when you are in an agitated panic?

O: What 'O' means turned into stone: but is used for people who are callous, unprogressive and set in their ways?

K: What 'K' is a form of cabbage with curly leaves?

R: What 'R' is an edible part of certain fish, or a type of small deer?

T: What 'T' is a fishing vessel that uses a conical net dragged through the water?

A: What 'A' is the gemstone that is purple quartz?

E: What 'E' is an obsolete way of defining forty-five inches?

B: What 'B' are skippers, red admirals, and swallowtails?

P: What 'P' is a Greek letter and represents the number 3.142 in mathematics?

D: What 'D' are the Schottische and the Gay Gordons?

N: What 'N' is the number above the line in vulgar fractions?

J: What 'J' is a fibre, once manufactured in Dundee and now in Calcutta?

S: What 'S' is a narrow slit window in a church wall, or a word for being crosseyed?

H: What 'H' is a musical instrument also known as a clavecin?

U: What 'U' hangs, roughly speaking, between the tonsils?

G: What 'G' is the village in Manhattan where the artistic trendies live?

M: What 'M' is Olivia's servant, who teases Malvolio in 'Twelfth Night'?

W: What 'W' do you raise when you succeed in getting money for some project?

C: What 'C', when it is Greek or Russian, is full of icons?

L: What 'L' was ruled by Idris I when it first became independent in 1951?

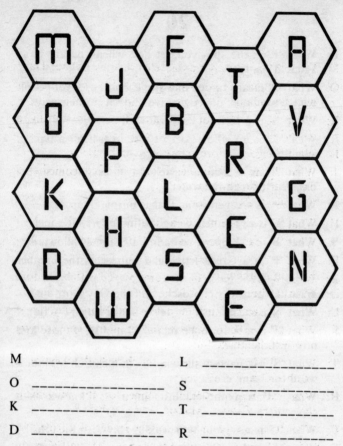

M _____   L _____

O _____   S _____

K _____   T _____

D _____   R _____

J _____   C _____

P _____   E _____

H _____   A _____

W _____   V _____

F _____   G _____

B _____   N _____

M: What 'M' is the day that is celebrated as Labour Day?

O: What 'O' means to do what you're told – if anyone ever does nowadays?

K: What 'K' is the foot operated lever for starting a motorbike?

D: What 'D' goes before centre, line and cert?

J: What 'J' sits in a box, has a foreman, is controlled by a bailiff and brings a verdict?

P: What 'P' is a cat's foot?

H: What 'H' was the pirate captain in Peter Pan?

W: What 'W' can be bay, sash, bow or casement?

F: What 'F' precedes glove, hunt and trot?

B: What 'B' is the name of the game played with battledore and shuttlecock?

L: What 'L' can be Russian, patent and Moroccan?

S: What 'S' are the translations shown on the screen during a foreign language film?

T: What 'T' in music means to change the key of a composition?

R: What 'R' was the Italian name for the movement fostered by Cavour, Mazzini and Garibaldi?

C: What 'C' is a type of tank, or the leader of a tribe?

E: What 'E' was first distilled by Johann Maria Farina in the 18th century?

A: What 'A' was a female warrior in Greek legend, and is a South American river?

V: What 'V' was the Fair invented by Bunyan and used by Thackeray?

G: What 'G' means serious as an adjective or a hole in the ground as a noun?

N: What 'N' is where some Lapplanders live?

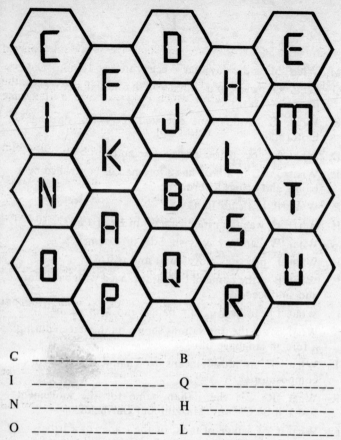

C _____

I _____

N _____

O _____

F _____

K _____

A _____

P _____

D _____

J _____

B _____

Q _____

H _____

L _____

S _____

R _____

E _____

M _____

T _____

U _____

C: What 'C' is the series in which Russell Hunter played 'Lonley'?

I: What 'I' is the name given to three layers of the atmosphere, one of which is known as the 'Heaviside Layer'?

N: What 'N' comes before out, club and gown?

O: What 'O' is a person whose conscience will not allow him to take part in war?

F: What 'F' is hair that is a kinky mass of very tight curls?

K: What 'K' was the nickname given to the election of 1900?

A: What 'A' is an allowance paid to a divorced or separated spouse?

P: What 'P' are trains that carry people rather than goods?

D: What 'D' was the impresario of the 'Ballets Russes' in the early 1900s?

J: What 'J' is the French word used for any ornamental pot or stand for displaying growing plants?

B: What 'B' are Oxfordshire's most famous cakes?

Q: What 'Q' is what the Americans call a shirker?

H: What 'H' is the branch of medicine whose motto is 'Like cures Like'?

L: What 'L' was a leader of the English Reformation and was burnt with Ridley in 1555?

S: What 'S' goes before onion, board, and chicken?

R: What 'R' is a long exchange of strokes in tennis before a point is won?

E: What 'E' are little holes for laces?

M: What 'M' are the spirits that are sold for burning, and are mauve?

T: What 'T' is a small wig for a bald patch?

U: What 'U' was a famous painter of street scenes in Montmartre who died in 1955?

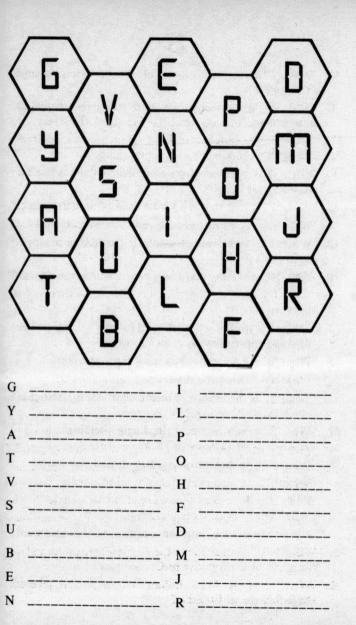

G _____   I _____

Y _____   L _____

A _____   P _____

T _____   O _____

V _____   H _____

S _____   F _____

U _____   D _____

B _____   M _____

E _____   J _____

N _____   R _____

G: What 'G' is a bridge from a ship to shore or a passage between seats?

Y: What 'Y' is an American National Park that isn't Yellowstone?

A: What 'A' was daughter of James II and Queen of Great Britain?

T: What 'T' is where soldiers sleep when they are under canvas?

V: What 'V' is a raptorial bird with a naked head and neck?

S: What 'S' goes before Armada, onion and guitar?

U: On what 'U' was the character of Leopold Bloom based, by James Joyce?

B: What 'B' is the suit you are said to be wearing when you are naked?

E: What 'E' is used to decorate the robes of judges, peers and royalty, and has little black tails all over it?

N: What 'N' is very abundant in the air, and is a gas?

I: What 'I' can be corn, summer or rope-trick?

L: What 'L' is what the portside used to be called?

P: What 'P' is Shaw's play in which Professor Higgins creates a 'Lady' out of a flower seller?

O: What 'O' goes before post, look and standing?

H: What 'H' contains most of the Serpentine and is a park?

F: What 'F' is probably the most famous basset hound in Britain?

D: What 'D' is known as a moke, a dicky or a neddy?

M: What 'M' is a secret society of dubious reputation originating in Sicily but now active in the USA as well?

J: What 'J' is a contraction of the Hebrew for Joshua and is the name of the founder of Christianity?

R: What 'R' is the West Indian religion which reveres Haile Selassie of Ethiopia?

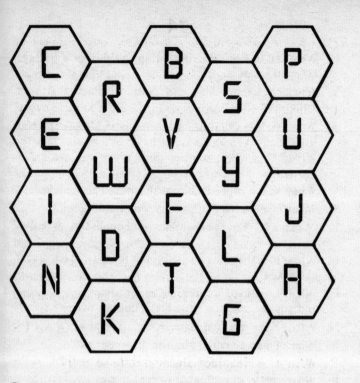

C _____ F _____

E _____ T _____

I _____ S _____

N _____ Y _____

R _____ L _____

W _____ G _____

D _____ P _____

K _____ U _____

B _____ J _____

V _____ A _____

C: What 'C' is the officer in command of a regiment of which Blimp and Bogey were examples?

E: What 'E' laid the foundations of modern geometry a long time ago?

I: What 'I' was the first name of the great Jesuit, Loyola?

N: What 'N' is the proper name for both the notch in an arrow and the notches at each end of a bow to take the string?

R: What 'R' is the sort of meeting where dogs or horses compete?

W: What 'W' means rich?

D: What 'D' is the two on dice, or an even score at tennis?

K: What 'K' is the fuel used for turbojets, turboprops and turbo fans?

B: What 'B' was in her prime in a novel by Muriel Spark?

V: What 'V' makes a soft smooth glove, in which you find an iron hand?

F: What 'F' became Mondale's running mate in the US Presidential election?

T: What 'T' left 'Grange Hill' and is trying his 'luck' in the big world?

S: What 'S' was a 1960s pop group, or a wooden structure for execution?

Y: What 'Y' produces little red berries and wood used for making bows?

L: What 'L' is another name for a maze?

G: What 'G' is an apparatus for producing hot water, or a hot spring?

P: What 'P' is to explore a region for gold?

U: What 'U' is another name for the constellation known as 'Charles's Wain', or the 'Great Bear'?

J: What 'J' is a piece of an animal's body, as cut up for the table?

A: What 'A' was a faithful friend of Aeneas?

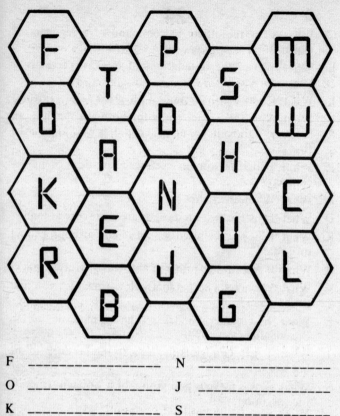

F   ——————————
O   ——————————
K   ——————————
R   ——————————
T   ——————————
A   ——————————
E   ——————————
B   ——————————
P   ——————————
D   ——————————

N   ——————————
J   ——————————
S   ——————————
H   ——————————
U   ——————————
G   ——————————
M   ——————————
W   ——————————
C   ——————————
L   ——————————

F: What 'F' is metaphorically said to be laid on with a trowel?

O: What 'O' goes before haul, look and board?

K: What 'K' is applied to close cousins because of the way they are greeted?

R: What 'R' means to ransack or search in an untidy way?

T: What 'T' is someone who stays away from school without good reason?

A: What 'A' is habitually forgetful and often a professor?

E: What 'E' is called a wapiti or a moose, in North America?

B: What 'B' is a stock character in 'Cinderella', or a hotel page?

P: What 'P' is a ride on the back and shoulders of another?

D: What 'D' wrote 'The Three Musketeers'?

N: What 'N' indicates a married woman's maiden name?

J: What 'J' is a fool or clown in Shakespeare?

S: What 'S' was the capital city in Zimbabwe, now called Harare? (pronounced Ha-rar-ree)

H: What 'H' were French Calvinists persecuted from the 16th century onwards?

U: What 'U' is the opposite of beautiful?

G: What 'G' is the cape nearest to England on the French coast, beloved of Channel swimmers?

M: What 'M' is the reporter played by John Thaw in a series that bears the reporter's name?

W: What 'W' is sometimes called Mountain Dew, and is a Scottish drink?

C: What 'C' was a British Premier at the time of the Munich crisis?

L: What 'L' is a town with a population of more than five million in Peru?

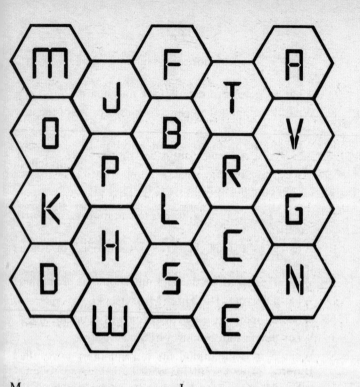

M _____   L _____

O _____   S _____

K _____   T _____

D _____   R _____

J _____   C _____

P _____   E _____

H _____   A _____

W _____   V _____

F _____   G _____

B _____   N _____

26

M: What 'M' means not shiny, having no lustre and is applied to paint?

O: What 'O' was King of the Fairies in 'Midsummer Night's Dream'?

K: What 'K' is Superman's home planet?

D: What 'D' is toothpaste?

J: What 'J' is a creeping plant called moneywort?

P: What 'P' describes the small amount of cash in an office or a non-commissioned officer in the Navy?

H: What 'H' is the generally used name for the low countries, or Netherlands?

W: What 'W' is the first name of Shirley MacLaine's brother who calls himself Beatty?

F: What 'F' was Marlowe's and Goethe's hero who sold his soul to the devil?

B: What 'B' is a pair of pheasants, or other game?

L: What 'L' is the name of the political party that succeeded the Whigs?

S: What 'S' is the building for housing horses, or the collective name for the racehorses belonging to one owner?

T: What 'T' is the usual nursery word for stomach?

R: What 'R' is the outside of a cheese or the peel of an orange?

C: What 'C' is in charge of a lifeboat?

E: What 'E' can be bald, golden or American?

A: What 'A' precedes strip, force, and cushion?

V: What 'V' was a name invented by Swift for one of his correspondents, afterwards borne by Virginia Woolf's sister?

G: What 'G' is the characteristic expression worn by a Cheshire cat?

N: What 'N' is the great turkey-producing county of England?

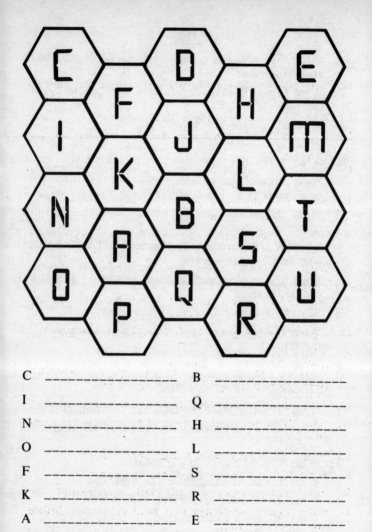

C _____   B _____

I _____   Q _____

N _____   H _____

O _____   L _____

F _____   S _____

K _____   R _____

A _____   E _____

P _____   M _____

D _____   T _____

J _____   U _____

27

C: What 'C' among Chaucer's Pilgrims told the story of Patient Griselda?

I: What 'I' are your cutting teeth in the front?

N: What 'N' is an open fabric, knotted into meshes, for catching fish?

O: What 'O' is to take possession of territory by running over it with military force?

F: What 'F' is the name given to the leaf-like foliage of ferns?

K: What 'K' was a painter whose works of art unexpectedly fetched more than a quarter of a million at auction?

A: What 'A' is a narrow lane that can be blind, bowling or skittle?

P: What 'P' is a perfect diamond of over 100 carats, or any supremely excellent person or thing?

D: What 'D' comes before treat, courage, and cheese?

J: What 'J' comes before snipe, ass and daw?

B: What 'B' in the northern part of the Northern Hemisphere is the shallowest of all the seas?

Q: What 'Q' is a voice with a shaking or tremulous quality?

H: What 'H' is the common noun of assemblage for goats and cows?

L: What 'L' is what cloth is woven on?

S: What 'S' comes before blast, bag and paper?

R: What 'R' means to roam, or to talk incoherently?

E: What 'E' are substances that need detonation before causing destruction?

M: What 'M' is a metallic element that is liquid at room temperature?

T: What 'T' follows oxygen, bell and circus?

U: What 'U' sometimes has two teats and sometimes four?

G _____ I _____

Y _____ L _____

A _____ P _____

T _____ O _____

V _____ H _____

S _____ F _____

U _____ D _____

B _____ M _____

E _____ J _____

N _____ R _____

28

G: What 'G' was unified by Bismarck?

Y: What 'Y' is a Republic washed by the Adriatic Sea?

A: What 'A' is the surgical removal of a limb?

T: What 'T' can be called Natterjacks?

V: What 'V' are main cavities of the heart?

S: What 'S' comes before level, gum and lamp?

U: What 'U' made 'Love's Great Adventure'?

B: What 'B' was the title taken by Maxwell Aitken, the newspaper magnate, when he was made a peer?

E: What 'E' is the nickname for the device that produces winning Premium Bond numbers?

N: What 'N' are, or were, Poor Clares?

I: What 'I' is a cricketer called Botham?

L: What 'L' is a mollusc with a pyramid-shaped shell which is proverbial for clinging to rocks?

P: What 'P' was one of the seven hills of Rome?

O: What 'O' is a twentieth of a pint of fluid?

H: What 'H' was the King who lost his life at Hastings in 1066?

F: What 'F' is the commonest computer language used for scientific programmes?

D: What 'D' is a megalith like a cromlech?

M: What 'M' is a disease of glands, in the neck (and sometimes elsewhere), called parotitis?

J: What 'J' is a remote place to which a person is humorously consigned, mentioned in the book of Samuel?

R: What 'R' is the rag that is said to annoy a bull?

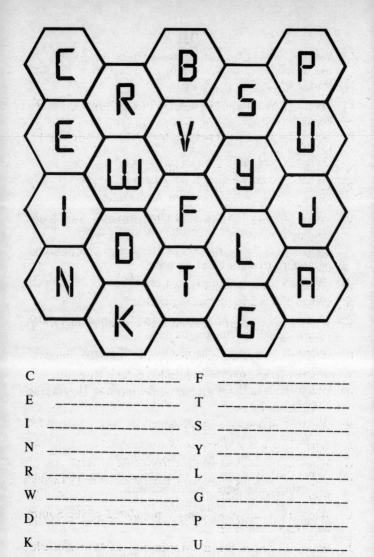

C _____ F _____

E _____ T _____

I _____ S _____

N _____ Y _____

R _____ L _____

W _____ G _____

D _____ P _____

K _____ U _____

B _____ J _____

V _____ A _____

29

C: What 'C' is the Christian name shared by the inventor of the hovercraft and the author of 'The Lady's Not for Burning'?

E: What 'E' is the commonest of the various forms of alcohol?

I: What 'I' is a parade of persons from whom a suspect is to be picked out?

N: What 'N' is an egg that is really fresh?

R: What 'R' is the light at the back of a vehicle, which comes on when you back?

W: What 'W' made Harrogate, Baden-Baden and Bath famous as Spas?

D: What 'D' is a cyclone or low-pressure system in meteorology?

K: What 'K' is the marsh marigold?

B: What 'B' is the father of Zowie?

V: What 'V' was the most famous 17th century painter from Delft?

F: What 'F' is the final position of a breakdance routine?

T: What 'T' is the type of dog called a Jack Russell?

S: What 'S' is the game played by one person, or a single stone diamond ring?

Y: What 'Y' makes beer alcoholic?

L: What 'L' is a Royal Spa in Warwickshire?

G: What 'G' is the flesh you get from cold or fear?

P: What 'P' was the dominant federal state in Germany from 1871 to 1918?

U: What 'U' is the most densely populated of the South American countries?

J: What 'J' began life in Martinique as Mademoiselle Tascher de la Pagerie, and ended up an Empress?

A: What 'A' is a bet on several successive races or a storage battery?

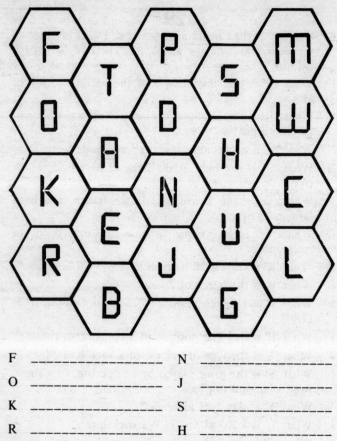

F _____   N _____

O _____   J _____

K _____   S _____

R _____   H _____

T _____   U _____

A _____   G _____

E _____   M _____

B _____   W _____

P _____   C _____

D _____   L _____

30

F: What 'F' is the other two-syllable word for fluter, flutist or flute-player?

O: What 'O' has a great Nebula in the hilt of his sword?

K: What 'K' are sheepshanks and clove hitches?

R: What 'R' was the surname of the Russian Royal Dynasty until 1917?

T: What 'T' was the Welsh family that gave us five Sovereigns?

A: What 'A' is a landlord who doesn't live on his property, or a person who doesn't go to his work?

E: What 'E' is to preserve a body from decay with oils and spices?

B: What 'B' comes before man, seller, and foot forward?

P: What 'P' spent a long time trying to form a government in Israel in August 1984?

D: What 'D' was the city where Mrs Gandhi was assassinated?

N: What 'N' is the group of theatres which includes the Lyttelton and the Olivier?

J: What 'J' is another word for 'to stick', or to block by crowding?

S: What 'S' is a sign of the Zodiac that has a sting in its tail?

H: What 'H' is home to a bee?

U: What 'U' is the husband of an Aunt?

G: What 'G' was William, the prize-winning author of 'The Rites of Passage'?

M: What 'M' is a male pop singer who shares his name with Miss Monroe?

W: What 'W' is where a belt usually goes?

C: What 'C' is a breed of tiny Mexican dog?

L: What 'L' is the only member of the cat family to have a mane?

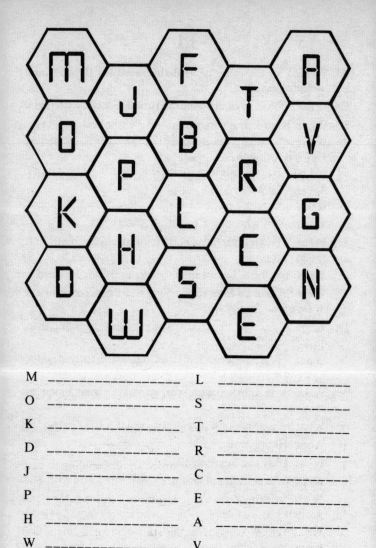

M _____   L _____

O _____   S _____

K _____   T _____

D _____   R _____

J _____   C _____

P _____   E _____

H _____   A _____

W _____   V _____

F _____   G _____

B _____   N _____

31

M: What 'M' is the light metal that burns with a brilliant white light?

O: What 'O' is a double-reed instrument in the woodwind section of an orchestra?

K: What 'K' is all of a soldier's gear, which is often inspected?

D: What 'D' goes before wit, weather and wine?

J: What 'J' goes with flotsam?

P: What 'P' is the practice of reading character from lines in the hand?

H: What 'H' comes before fly, guards and play?

W: What 'W' was the first great leader of Poland's Solidarity?

F: What 'F' is a celebration in Spain or Mexico?

B: What 'B' comes before thorn, berry and bird?

L: What 'L' means gain or profit and is nearly always filthy?

S: What 'S' was the character played by Olivia Newton-John in 'Grease'?

T: What 'T', eaten as a vegetable, was once known as a love apple?

R: What 'R' falls 'Mainly in the Plains'?

C: What 'C' is another word for choirboy?

E: What 'E' is the statuette awarded to outstanding shows, or performers, on television?

A: What 'A' are gibbons, orang-utans, chimpanzees and gorillas?

V: What 'V' in America is the state known as 'The Old Dominion'?

G: What 'G' is also known as plumbago or black lead?

N: What 'N' is the town in Galilee where Jesus was a carpenter?

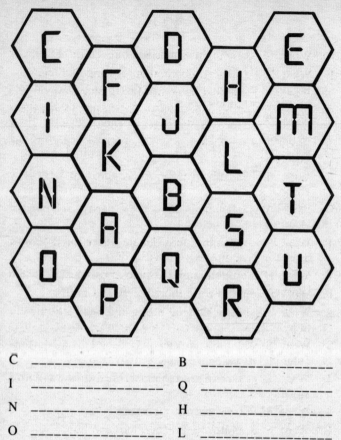

C _____ B _____
I _____ Q _____
N _____ H _____
O _____ L _____
F _____ S _____
K _____ R _____
A _____ E _____
P _____ M _____
D _____ T _____
J _____ U _____

32

C: What 'C' is a crack in a glacier or an ice-sheet?

I: What 'I' is a Mozart opera about a King of Crete?

N: What 'N' is the first name of Mr St John Stevas?

O: What 'O' is a book size where the sheet is folded three times to produce sixteen pages of eight sheets?

F: What 'F' is the first page of a newspaper, where all the big stories go?

K: What 'K' was the Anglo Saxon kingdom settled by Hengist and Horsa?

A: What 'A' is a building endowed by charity, to house the elderly poor?

P: What 'P' is the umbelliferous plant whose leaves flavour a white sauce often served with cod?

D: What 'D' is Offa supposed to have constructed in the 8th century as a boundary for Mercia?

J: What 'J' is the name given to God in the Old Testament?

B: What 'B' was murdered on December 29th, 1170 in Canterbury?

Q: What 'Q' is an adult female pedigree cat?

H: What 'H' is thought to have married Eva Braun during the last days of their lives?

L: What 'L' are the organs of respiration?

S: What 'S' goes before lavender, legs and lion?

R: What 'R' was the parapet of a castle from which boiling oil and arrows were despatched?

E: What 'E' is affected by astigmatism?

M: What 'M' is the large tent often used for weddings and fêtes?

T: What 'T' is a game that consists of snapping little discs into a cup?

U: What 'U' comes from the Greek for 'no place' and is the name of Sir Thomas More's imaginary country?

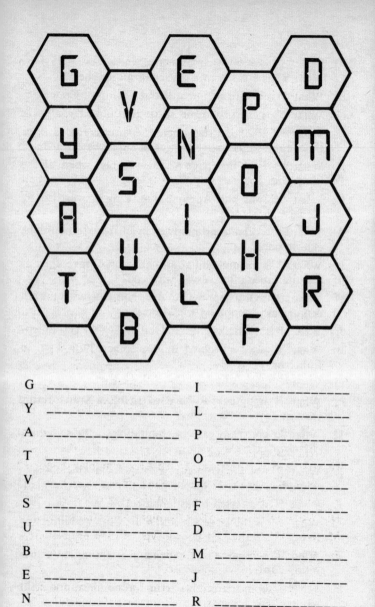

G _____	I _____
Y _____	L _____
A _____	P _____
T _____	O _____
V _____	H _____
S _____	F _____
U _____	D _____
B _____	M _____
E _____	J _____
N _____	R _____

33

G: What 'G' is the town in Somerset which has a holy thorn that flowers at Christmas?

Y: What 'Y' is last year or earlier?

A: What 'A' is the continent of origin of the tomato and potato?

T: What 'T' are minion, bourgeois, and ruby, which are used by printers?

V: What 'V' is rapidity of motion and comes after actual, circular, and terminal?

S: What 'S' goes before head, test and graft?

U: What 'U' is a diamond in the rough state?

B: What 'B' is a quiz hosted by Jim Bowen in which there are questions and dart-playing?

E: What 'E' is a kind of mixed beer, an un-castrated animal or something that is whole?

N: What 'N' was the American President who resigned in 1974?

I: What 'I' is bliss, where "Tis folly to be wise"?

L: What 'L' is commanded by a coxswain and rescues people?

P: What 'P' was Mohammed Ali Jinnah the first Governor General of?

O: What 'O' is the tale of a long journey made by a mythical Greek warrior?

H: What 'H' is a hurricane called Alex, who plays snooker?

F: What 'F' was the nickname given to people seeking gold in California in the middle of the 19th century?

D: What 'D' can be seven sins, nightshade and serious?

M: What 'M' is the best known type of map projection?

J: What 'J' is named after Leyden and is a primitive form of electric battery or condenser?

R: What 'R' is defined as grim when meaning death personified?

C _____ F _____

E _____ T _____

I _____ S _____

N _____ Y _____

R _____ L _____

W _____ G _____

D _____ P _____

K _____ U _____

B _____ J _____

V _____ A

34

C: What 'C' was comic actor/producer, Sir Charles Spencer, who died in 1977?

E: What 'E' was the father of Methuselah and is Mr Powell, MP?

I: What 'I' was once Mesopotamia and is now at war?

N: What 'N' is ten times ten, minus ten?

R: What 'R' is a garden tool for collecting up leaves or breaking the soil's surface?

W: What 'W' is a pattern in blue, first seen on English china in the 18th century?

D: What 'D' is the needle you use for mending socks?

K: What 'K' do doctors find renal calculi or stones?

B: What 'B' goes before foot, back, and faced?

V: What 'V' is an old soldier or a very old car?

F: What 'F' is the popular name for naval underwater demolition teams?

T: What 'T' is the Jewish name for the Old Testament of the Bible?

S: What 'S' was Wurzel Gummidge who stood in a field to frighten the birds?

Y: What 'Y' is a slang term in Britain for all Americans: but in the USA means only Northerners?

L: What 'L' is the mountain in Syria round which many of the Druse live?

G: What 'G' is the unit of heredity in the chromosomes?

P: What 'P' is a baby that was born before the expected time?

U: What 'U' means against the current or nearer the source?

J: What 'J' said, 'You ain't heard nothin' yet' in the first talking picture?

A: What 'A' is a door that is not quite shut?

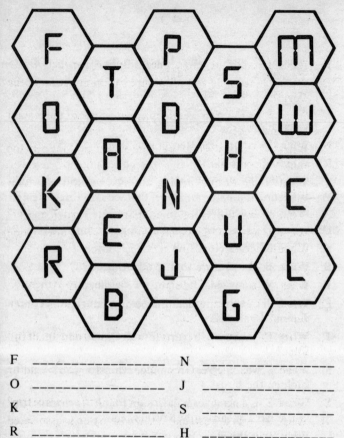

F _____   N _____

O _____   J _____

K _____   S _____

R _____   H _____

T _____   U _____

A _____   G _____

E _____   M _____

B _____   W _____

P _____   C _____

D _____   L _____

35

F: What 'F' could be dance, mezzanine or parquet?

O: What 'O' are used to pull ploughs in many parts of the world?

K: What 'K' is the Aga who is spiritual leader of the Ismaili Muslims?

R: What 'R' is a tiny island that comes next to 'Malin' in the shipping forecasts?

T: What 'T' between Wapping and Rotherhithe was built by Brunel?

A: What 'A' means to shorten or abbreviate written matter?

E: What 'E' used to be the internationally recognised name for Southern Ireland?

B: What 'B' do you do when you sneak off?

P: What 'P' slew Medusa and gave the head to Athena?

D: What 'D' was murdered after an intrigue between Bothwell and Mary Stuart?

N: What 'N' is called 'Nanette', and is married to Bryan Forbes?

J: What 'J' was the part of an ass used as a weapon in the bible?

S: What 'S' is a person who hides on a ship to get a free trip?

H: What 'H' was the astronomer whose name is associated with 'Red Shift'?

U: What 'U' is an imaginary land where everything is perfect?

G: What 'G' means to strike or snap teeth together in rage or pain?

M: What 'M' was the Italian who largely invented radio?

W: What 'W' goes with beetle, and has a thin end?

C: What 'C' is made into sauerkraut?

L: What 'L' can be cordate, palmate, or pinnate?

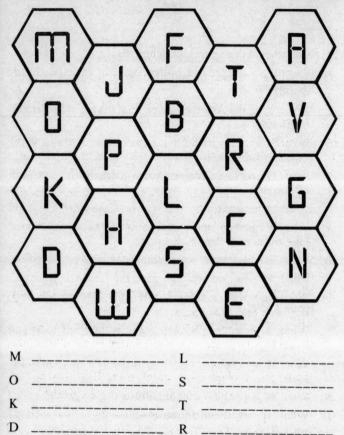

M _____   L _____

O _____   S _____

K _____   T _____

D _____   R _____

J _____   C _____

P _____   E _____

H _____   A _____

W _____   V _____

F _____   G _____

B _____   N _____

36

M: What 'M' is twelve o'clock when it's dark?

O: What 'O' is a gemstone which comes in varieties called fire and black?

K: What 'K' is a Russian fortress that houses the Soviet Government?

D: What 'D' goes with hose?

J: What 'J' is a nonsense poem by Lewis Carroll?

P: What 'P' was lost and regained by Milton?

H: What 'H' is a famous play in which Yorick and Horatio are characters?

W: What 'W' is the name by which Mr Collins, who wrote 'The Woman in White', is known?

F: What 'F' is the crypto-crystalline rock used by Neolithic man?

B: What 'B' is a sort of tree, a thing you pack shoes in, or a type of spanner?

L: What 'L' can be tiger, turk's cap, or madonna?

S: What 'S' was a man who was blinded by the Philistines and made to work in Gaza?

T: What 'T' is a name for privates in the British Army?

R: What 'R' is put in a dustbin and is useless trash?

C: What 'C' is made into marrons glacés?

E: What 'E' is the farm inhabited by the Sugdens?

A: What 'A' is a small town in Scotland where smokies come from?

V: What 'V' was the name of Gagarin's space vehicle in 1961?

G: What 'G' is the well known name for the very fast gaze-hound that hunts by sight?

N: What 'N' is another name for Holland?

C _____

I _____

N _____

O _____

F _____

K _____

A _____

P _____

D _____

J _____

B _____

Q _____

H _____

L _____

S _____

R _____

E _____

M _____

T _____

U _____

37

C: What 'C' is the noise made by a raven or a frog?

I: What 'I' is the name of a fairy opera by Gilbert and Sullivan?

N: What 'N' was the dominant political party in the 1930s in Germany?

O: What 'O' is a sky darkened by many clouds?

F: What 'F' means to go often or habitually, to a place, or a house?

K: What 'K' is an investment in the form of a foreign coin?

A: What 'A' is a word like amiable, meaning friendly, or showing good will?

P: What 'P' was the name of the first man-made vehicle to quit the solar system?

D: What 'D' was the famous vampire created by Bram Stoker?

J: What 'J' was the handsome and respected half of horrible Edward Hyde?

B: What 'B', coloured gold, used to hang in threes outside a pawnbroker's establishment?

Q: What 'Q' are the spines of a porcupine?

H: What 'H' is the German Port that gave its name to fried minced steak?

L: What 'L' was a dreaded disease in medieval times, but is now fortunately getting rarer?

S: What 'S' goes before fastener, shot and dragon?

R: What 'R' were the rocks around which the ragged rascal ran?

E: What 'E' is a town famous for its salts and racecourse?

M: What 'M' was produced in 1848 by Engels and Marx for the communists?

T: What 'T' is the fifth day of the week?

U: What 'U' takes the place of another; usually a ruler and usually by force?

G _____ I _____

Y _____ L _____

A _____ P _____

T _____ O _____

V _____ H _____

S _____ F _____

U _____ D _____

B _____ M _____

E _____ J _____

N _____ R _____

38

G: What 'G' is a mythical lord who writes in 'Private Eye'?

Y: What 'Y' is Tokyo's seaport?

A: What 'A' is rung at morn, noon and sunset?

T: What 'T' was Maggie Tulliver's brother in 'Mill on the Floss'?

V: What 'V' means crafty or cunning like a fox?

S: What 'S' goes before book, line, and teller?

U: What 'U' means wrong way up?

B: What 'B' starred in the films 'Help' and 'A Hard Day's Night'?

E: What 'E' did Ensa provide for the troops in the last war?

N: What 'N' is the largest republic of Central America?

I: What 'I' once included the areas now known as Bangladesh and Pakistan?

L: What 'L' is a vegetable that comes long, cos or cabbage?

P: What 'P' is any journal published at regular intervals?

O: What 'O' on the Isis is a city of dreaming spires?

H: What 'H' is the double seat on the back of an elephant?

F: What 'F' goes before trot, glove, and hunt?

D: What 'D' has games called muggins, all threes, threes and fives, or sniff?

M: What 'M' wants to clean up television and is called Whitehouse?

J: What 'J' was 'always tomorrow, never today' much to Alice's mystification?

R: What 'R' is another name for Mac?

C   _____
E   _____
I   _____
N   _____
R   _____
W   _____
D   _____
K   _____
B   _____
V   _____

F   _____
T   _____
S   _____
Y   _____
L   _____
G   _____
P   _____
U   _____
J   _____
A   _____

39

C: What 'C' is often used to treat the water in swimming baths?

E: What 'E' are Exonians native inhabitants of?

I: What 'I' is a slight knowledge, a hint, a suspicion?

N: What 'N' is the first name of a BBC presenter called Edmonds?

R: What 'R' wears a top-hat and tails and announces circus acts?

W: What 'W' is an official in charge of prisoners in a jail?

D: What 'D' is the unit of currency in Singapore?

K: What 'K' was a Soviet premier called Nikita, who died in 1971?

B: What 'B' is a compartment for oil or coal in a ship, or a hazard in golf?

V: What 'V' means strong, intense or glaring when applied to colour or light?

F: What 'F' is raised and lowered on poles?

T: What 'T' is a tiny drink, or a small toddler?

S: What 'S' is a description of your youthful days, or a dish of raw vegetables?

Y: What 'Y' is what a ship does when it deviates temporarily and irregularly from course?

L: What 'L' is a member of the Genus Allium, and is a symbol of Wales?

G: What 'G' is the 'G' of the probably doomed GLC?

P: What 'P' is a doctor who does medical, rather than surgical treatment?

U: What 'U' is a student who hasn't yet got a degree?

J: What 'J' is the most important vegetable fibre after cotton and flax, and is used to make sacks?

A: What 'A' is one sort of accent in written French or means shrewd?

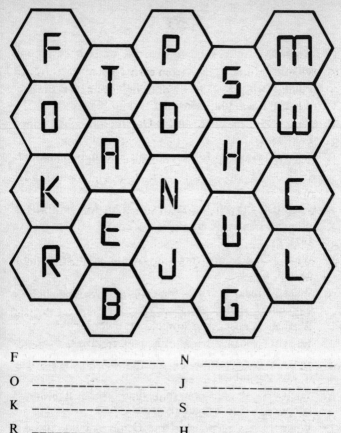

F   _____   N   _____

O   _____   J   _____

K   _____   S   _____

R   _____   H   _____

T   _____   U   _____

A   _____   G   _____

E   _____   M   _____

B   _____   W   _____

P   _____   C   _____

D   _____   L   _____

40

F: What 'F' can be hunted from early November to April?

O: What 'O' has a reputation for bringing bad luck, in spite of being a beautiful gemstone?

K: What 'K' is a better word for Osculation?

R: What 'R' had the first man Friday to help him?

T: What 'T' is a regular-shaped ancient burial mound?

A: What 'A' was the name given to those who wanted to do away with slavery?

E: What 'E' is a seat that fires an airman to safety, with a bit of luck?

B: What 'B' was one of the seven dwarfs?

P: What 'P' is the height of a musical note, or the field for a football match?

D: What 'D' is the title borne by Naomi James?

N: What 'N' are three detached masses of chalk off the Isle of Wight, one with a lighthouse?

J: What 'J' was the egg in a famous play by Peter Nicholls?

S: What 'S' is a celebrity in the film world, or a bright object in the sky?

H: What 'H' are chloride, bromide, iodide and fluoride?

U: What 'U' is called a brolly?

G: What 'G' is the adjective that used to be applied to World War One?

M: What 'M' goes before castle, speech, over, and voyage?

W: What 'W' is the nose of a missile that contains the explosive?

C: What 'C' means horse-soldiers or mounted troops?

L: What 'L' is sore when you have a sore throat?

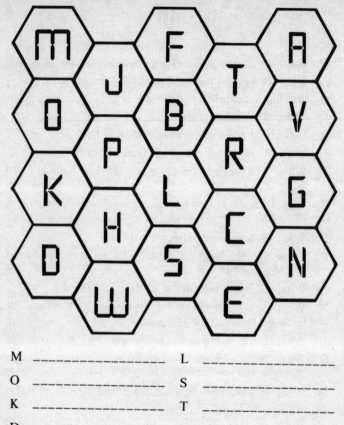

M _____   L _____

O _____   S _____

K _____   T _____

D _____   R _____

J _____   C _____

P _____   E _____

H _____   A _____

W _____   V _____

F _____   G _____

B _____   N _____

41

M: What 'M' is one who suffers death for his beliefs?

O: What 'O' is the result of drawing too many cheques?

K: What 'K' is a brilliant blue and orange bird of English rivers?

D: What 'D' has a capital called Copenhagen?

J: What 'J' is the quality of four men created by Edgar Wallace?

P: What 'P' is a name for the first five books of the Old Testament?

H: What 'H' is a small group of houses in the country, or Shakespeare's gloomy Dane?

W: What 'W' was the surname adopted by the British Royal Family in 1917?

F: What 'F' is borne by something that fructifies?

B: What 'B' is the most famous library in Oxford?

L: What 'L' is the popular descriptive name of the disease produced by tetanus?

S: What 'S' is an herb, or a person with much wisdom?

T: What 'T' comes after jog, rising and sitting?

R: What 'R' was Isaac's wife, in the bible, or a fictitious character created by Daphne Du Maurier?

C: What 'C' is a thrombosis of the blood vessels of the heart?

E: What 'E' was Ron's girlfriend and Mr Glum's prospective daughter-in-law in a classic radio series?

A: What 'A' was the bird that the Ancient Mariner killed and had to wear around his neck?

V: What 'V' is a small venomous snake?

G: What 'G' start getting shot on August 12th each year?

N: What 'N' is where you go to see the highest mountain in the world?

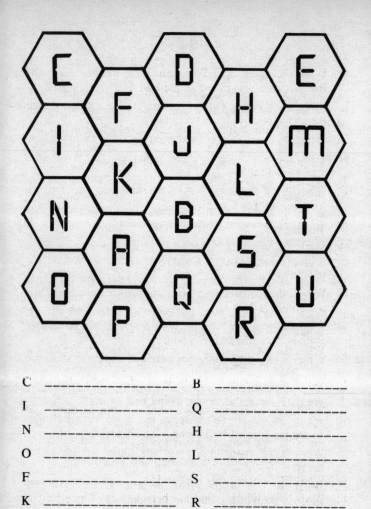

C	_____	B	_____
I	_____	Q	_____
N	_____	H	_____
O	_____	L	_____
F	_____	S	_____
K	_____	R	_____
A	_____	E	_____
P	_____	M	_____
D	_____	T	_____
J	_____	U	_____

42

C: What 'C' was an American who championed the Indians, and was killed at the battle of the Alamo?

I: What 'I' is a person who puts money into a business or buys stocks and shares?

N: What 'N' is left if you take eighteen from thirty-seven?

O: What 'O' is a word for egg-shaped and the name of a cricket ground?

F: What 'F' is a match played for pleasure only, not in competition for a cup?

K: What 'K' is a utensil for boiling water?

A: What 'A' is a square measure of land?

P: What 'P' is another word for pacify, conciliate, or propitiate?

D: What 'D' is the name given to metal containers for transporting oil?

J: What 'J' was the heroine who married Mr Rochester after he was blinded in a fire?

B: What 'B' is a place in Derbyshire that has given its name to a tart?

Q: What 'Q' is to engage in contention, or fall out?

H: What 'H' is the presumed author of 'The Iliad' and 'Odyssey'?

L: What 'L' is a lump of wood for the fire?

S: What 'S' goes before bone, cup and pump?

R: What 'R' is a Ranee's husband?

E: What 'E' is the tree that has been killed off by a fungus and a bark beetle?

M: What 'M' is where Humphrey Bogart ran Rick's Café, in the film 'Casablanca'?

T: What 'T' is a town in West Africa whose name is used to represent any very distant place?

U: What 'U' is a childish way of bowling a cricket ball?

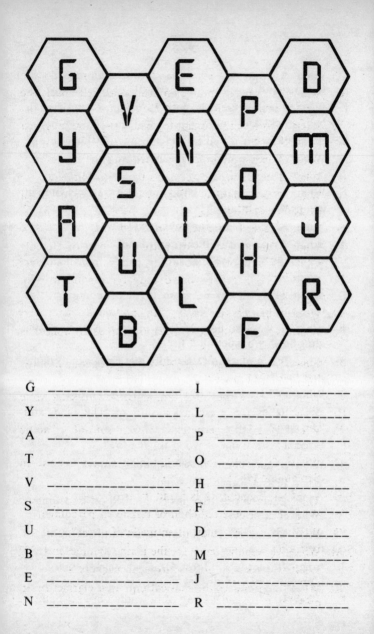

G	_____	I	_____
Y	_____	L	_____
A	_____	P	_____
T	_____	O	_____
V	_____	H	_____
S	_____	F	_____
U	_____	D	_____
B	_____	M	_____
E	_____	J	_____
N	_____	R	_____

43

G: What 'G' was the politician who said he'd 'back the masses against the classes' in 1886?

Y: What 'Y' is a small circular toy which rises and falls on a piece of string?

A: What 'A' is the home of the Archers?

T: What 'T' is Dennis Waterman's name in 'Minder'?

V: What 'V' is to harden rubber by chemical means, often by adding sulphur?

S: What 'S' goes before beam, spot and set?

U: What 'U' is an actor who played the part of Hercule Poirot in 'Death on the Nile'?

B: What 'B' is a pearly-vented tody tyrant and lives in America?

E: What 'E' goes before body, thing and day?

N: What 'N' is a river whose whirlpool rapids are almost as famous as its falls?

I: What 'I' was written in 1971 by John Lennon, and was No. 1 in 1981 again?

L: What 'L' were the most famous production of Mme de Sévigné?

P: What 'P' is the perpetually frozen subsoil in arctic regions?

O: What 'O' broke the world 1500 metres record in September 1983?

H: What 'H' is one if 'O' is 8 and 'C' is 6?

F: What 'F' is a deserted child of unknown parentage?

D: What 'D' is a lacy mat, often made of paper?

M: What 'M' was the venue for the main Olympics in 1980?

J: What 'J' goes with pokery, to mean trickery?

R: What 'R' produces the musical note in a clarinet or an oboe?

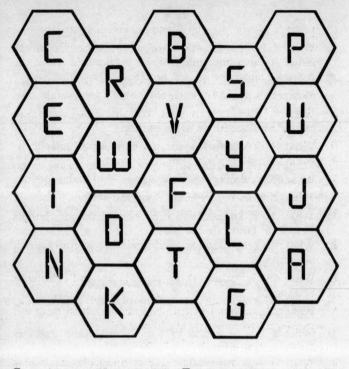

C   _____   F   _____

E   _____   T   _____

I   _____   S   _____

N   _____   Y   _____

R   _____   L   _____

W   _____   G   _____

D   _____   P   _____

K   _____   U   _____

B   _____   J   _____

V   _____   A   _____

44

C: What 'C' is the popular name for an integrated circuit?

E: What 'E' is Latin for 'therefore', and is part of Descartes' most famous statement?

I: What 'I' is the Scottish word for a small island and also a measure of length?

N: What 'N' was the heroine of 'War and Peace', and was played by Audrey Hepburn on film?

R: What 'R' is a string of beads used by Roman Catholics to count prayers?

W: What 'W' is a slang word for a right idiot and is the first name of a great traveller called Herbert?

D: What 'D' was the Italian poet who wrote 'The Divine Comedy'?

K: What 'K' is the roundish mark in timber where a branch used to be?

B: What 'B' is called Peter, and is Ireland's Foreign Minister?

V: What 'V' is a small British mammal of which there are species called bank-, field-, or water-?

F: What 'F' is a form in which snow falls?

T: What 'T' was our greatest civil engineer and has a new town in Shropshire named after him?

S: What 'S' is the blunt end of a ship?

Y: What 'Y' is a country bumpkin?

L: What 'L' were the machine-smashing workers of the early 19th century?

G: What 'G' is the sort of white sugar that isn't caster?

P: What 'P' means something done part at a time, or bit by bit?

U: What 'U' is a final offer, often delivered with a threat to break off relations?

J: What 'J' is the month in which the sun enters Aquarius?

A: What 'A' was the name of Mr Clare who married 'Tess of the D'Urbervilles', or is a celestial messenger?

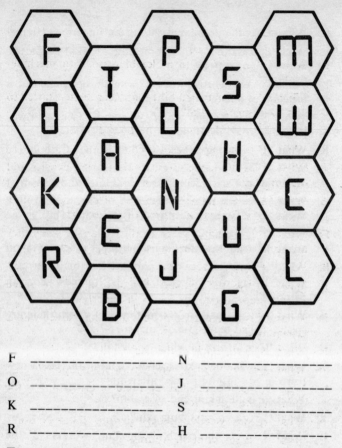

F _____

O _____

K _____

R _____

T _____

A _____

E _____

B _____

P _____

D _____

N _____

J _____

S _____

H _____

U _____

G _____

M _____

W _____

C _____

L _____

45

F: What 'F' is applied to a flexible disc with machine-readable data?

O: What 'O' is a fish eating bird that has recently started to nest again in Scotland?

K: What 'K' is an electrical or mechanical hooter?

R: What 'R' is the capital of Italy?

T: What 'T' is the name given to Hungarian gypsies and their music?

A: What 'A' is the name of the sort of dog that is often known as a German shepherd or sheepdog?

E: What 'E' is the name given to three planets, when they are seen in the West after sunset, and are taken for stars?

B: What 'B' was the poet who married Elizabeth Barrett?

P: What 'P' was the company founded in 1935 by Allen Lane to reprint famous books in paperback?

D: What 'D' is the literary word for a young maiden who is always in distress?

N: What 'N' is the back of the neck?

J: What 'J' is the 'Collins' who writes erotic books?

S: What 'S' has been called the Land of Cakes and is the home of the Loch Ness monster?

H: What 'H' was asked at the last minute to kiss Nelson?

U: What 'U' is sex-symbol, Andress?

G: What 'G' is *ursus horribilis*, a large bear?

M: What 'M' is the French National Anthem?

W: What 'W' is a name for the sort of sad film that makes you cry?

C: What 'C' is hung by rings on a rod at a window?

L: What 'L' are lakes called Lomond and Katrine, in Scotland?

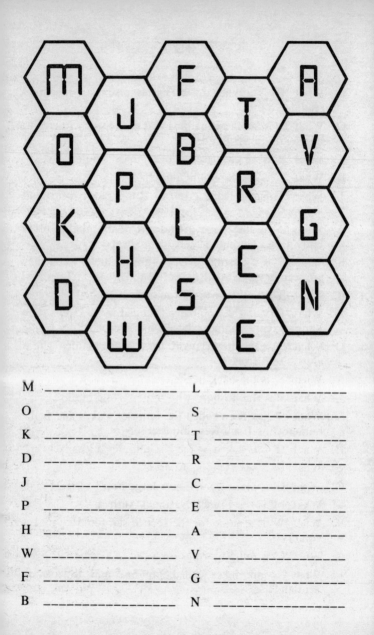

M _____

O _____

K _____

D _____

J _____

P _____

H _____

W _____

F _____

B _____

L _____

S _____

T _____

R _____

C _____

E _____

A _____

V _____

G _____

N _____

46

M: What 'M' is a hotel, specially adapted for people with cars?

O: What 'O' is a sacred story set to music?

K: What 'K' is defined as a hand held instrument for cutting?

D: What 'D' is the popular name for Sirius, the brightest star in the firmament?

J: What 'J' was the beloved disciple?

P: What 'P' follows stag, third and birthday?

H: What 'H' was a US President and is a vacuum cleaner?

W: What 'W' is a collective name for long-legged birds such as curlews, sandpipers and redshanks?

F: What 'F' comes before will, verse and fall?

B: What 'B' was the fourth astronaut to walk on the moon, or is a common vegetable?

L: What 'L' were 'Coronation', 'Merchant Navy' and 'King' class?

S: What 'S' is the Upper Chamber of both the French and the American legislature?

T: What 'T' do you have to pay to cross certain bridges?

R: What 'R' is the first name of a founder of the SDP, called Jenkins?

C: What 'C' is French for masterpiece?

E: What 'E' is, conventionally, the type of tinned milk that is unsweetened?

A: What 'A' can be right, obtuse or reflex?

V: What 'V' is a British nobleman, ranking above a Baron and below an Earl?

G: What 'G' is another word for rubbish or refuse?

N: What 'N' precedes wave, York and Year?

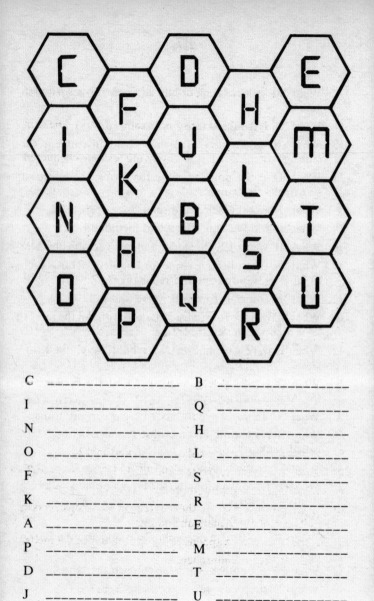

C _____ B _____

I _____ Q _____

N _____ H _____

O _____ L _____

F _____ S _____

K _____ R _____

A _____ E _____

P _____ M _____

D _____ T _____

J _____ U _____

47

C: What 'C' is a cut of beef, or part of a lathe, or a tap under the chin?

I: What 'I' are the toxic substances called Aldrin, Dieldrin and DDT?

N: What 'N' is signalled at sea by flying a single chequered flag?

O: What 'O' is the name of three English rivers, in Sussex, Yorkshire and the Fen country?

F: What 'F' is to predict or prophesy events?

K: What 'K' is a suburb of Tokyo that has given its name to a motorbike?

A: What 'A' is the re-arrangement of the letters from a word or set of words to form another?

P: What 'P' are the costermonger kings and queens?

D: What 'D' is the street where the Prime Minister lives?

J: What 'J' comes before baby, fish and bag?

B: What 'B' is a Scottish word for a young child?

Q: What 'Q' is half as long as a crotchet?

H: What 'H' is the name of Thora Hird's television series about the Salvation Army?

L: What 'L' is the long fast for Easter?

S: What 'S' goes before balance, tide and lock?

R: What 'R' is rickety, rotten and likely to fall to pieces?

E: What 'E' is something to make you sick?

M: What 'M' is a sort of shoe based on the soft deerskin footwear of the American Indians?

T: What 'T' is what happens to ice and snow when it melts?

U: What 'U' is to comprehend?

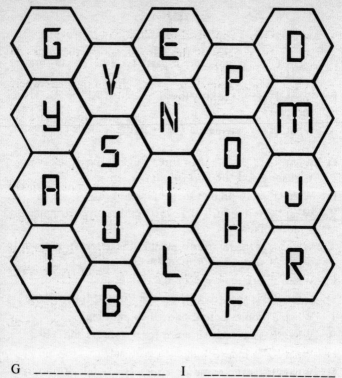

G _____
Y _____
A _____
T _____
V _____
S _____
U _____
B _____
E _____
N _____

I _____
L _____
P _____
O _____
H _____
F _____
D _____
M _____
J _____
R _____

48

G: What 'G' is a rope used to hold a tent in place?

Y: What 'Y' is part of the harness across the necks of working animals?

A: What 'A' is a saint whose name is that of the place where British golf is controlled?

T: What 'T' was the famous battle that took place on October 21, 1805?

V: What 'V' is not a consonant?

S: What 'S' comes after police, fire and railway?

U: What 'U' is the outcome, or the final issue, or a series of events?

B: What 'B' was one of the empires on which the sun never set?

E: What 'E' was conquered in 1953 by Hillary and Tensing?

N: What 'N' is a type of pliers, young children, or crab's claws?

I: What 'I' is said to be the sincerest form of flattery?

L: What 'L' is enlightening the world on Bedloe's Island, USA?

P: What 'P' is characteristic of goods that are likely to go bad in transit?

O: What 'O' was the friend and torturer of Winston Smith, in '1984'?

H: What 'H' has given his name to the celestial phenomenon that will be investigated by the Giotto Probe?

F: What 'F' is a golf match between two pairs of partners who play the same ball?

D: What 'D' was the name of the character who sang 'I'm Getting Married in the Morning' in 'My Fair Lady'?

M: What 'M' is a succulent fish that can be grey or red?

J: What 'J' is a solo folkdance popular in Scotland and Ireland?

R: What 'R' is a merry-go-round on a fairground, or an island round which traffic circulates?

C _____ F _____
E _____ T _____
I _____ S _____
N _____ Y _____
R _____ L _____
W _____ G _____
D _____ P _____
K _____ U _____
B _____ J _____
V _____ A _____

49

C: What 'C' is the country that was evacuated by French and Libyan forces in September 1984?

E: What 'E' is a courtesy title appended to a man's name, when addressing envelopes?

I: What 'I' is the I of IBA that was once ITA?

N: What 'N' is a word applied to a race horse, or anything else, that has been interfered with?

R: What 'R' describes an uncut diamond?

W: What 'W' is an East End district of London with a celebrated bell foundry?

D: What 'D' is where milk products are handled?

K: What 'K' was the first Mongol Emperor of China and the subject of a poem by Coleridge?

B: What 'B' is the 'Professional' played by Lewis Collins?

V: What 'V' was St Jerome's version of the Bible?

F: What 'F' are bleak, gudgeon and dace?

T: What 'T' is the site between Fleet Street and the Thames, occupied by lawyers since the 14th century?

S: What 'S' is the Institute of Theology, Science and Literature on the Left Bank of the Seine in Paris?

Y: What 'Y' is the singing noise made by Swiss mountaineers when the voice rises suddenly?

L: What 'L' is a specially honoured poet?

G: What 'G' do you do to a palm when you bribe somebody?

P: What 'P' is the archipelago between China and Borneo that has a capital called Manila?

U: What 'U' is the Gentleman of the Black Rod?

J: What 'J' was the great sea battle associated with Admiral Jellicoe in the First World War?

A: What 'A' is a card you may be said to have up your sleeve?

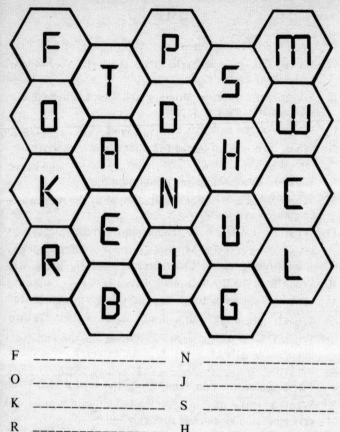

F _____   N _____

O _____   J _____

K _____   S _____

R _____   H _____

T _____   U _____

A _____   G _____

E _____   M _____

B _____   W _____

P _____   C _____

D _____   L _____

50

F: What 'F' is to lose or put away from memory?

O: What 'O' are (or were) the Hallé, the Boyd Neel and the Liverpool Phil?

K: What 'K' is the large, complicated joint in the leg?

R: What 'R' is a list of turns of duty?

T: What 'T' died in Kansas City in 1972 at the age of eighty-eight, as Ex-President of the USA?

A: What 'A' was the man in 'The Arabian Nights' who learnt to open a cave by saying 'Open Sesame'?

E: What 'E' was the preparation thought by the Alchemists to prolong life indefinitely?

B: What 'B' was the venue for the 1984 T.U.C. Conference?

P: What 'P' was an Athenian Statesman who directed the building of the Parthenon, and was also the name of a work by Shakespeare, but not the same man?

D: What 'D' is sweet, and grows on palms in North Africa?

N: What 'N' is probably Enid Blyton's best known character?

J: What 'J' is often a visible symptom of liver disease and causes you to look yellow?

S: What 'S' now means 'threatening' but used to mean 'on the left hand side'?

H: What 'H' is at the blunt end of a tintack?

U: What 'U' is the hand you get, when you get the better of someone?

G: What 'G' is known by its inhabitants as Hellas?

M: What 'M' is a theatrical performance that takes place in the afternoon?

W: What 'W' goes before machine, powder and up?

C: What 'C' are bits of television advertising?

L: What 'L' is a word for a golf shot or a place for storing hay?

M _____   L _____

O _____   S _____

K _____   T _____

D _____   R _____

J _____   C _____

P _____   E _____

H _____   A _____

W _____   V _____

F _____   G _____

B _____   N _____

51

M: What 'M' is the name of a Polish dance in 3 time, many of which were composed by Chopin?

O: What 'O' is working extra hours?

K: What 'K' is a garment called a filibeg?

D: What 'D' is, or should be, the foundation of a pizza?

J: What 'J' is a box that automatically plays records when a coin is inserted?

P: What 'P' is the line or mark, fixing the loadline of a merchant vessel?

H: What 'H' shows that silver is as it should be?

W: What 'W' is a man who practises sorcery, one of whom lived in the Land of Oz?

F: What 'F' are very close if they are called 'Dutch Cousins'?

B: What 'B' was the author of 'The Admirable Crichton' and 'Peter Pan'?

L: What 'L' is the kind of 'hanging about' that can be done with intent?

S: What 'S' is a pit, or a concrete tower in which greenstuff and molasses are stored for cattle food?

T: What 'T' goes before company, fund and territory?

R: What 'R' was a stack of hay or corn, usually thatched?

C: What 'C' were the royalists who were opposed to the Cromwellian Roundheads?

E: What 'E' means to breathe out, to come to an end, or to die?

A: What 'A' is the great land mass to which Liberia and Ethiopia belong?

V: What 'V' is a four-syllable word meaning a farewell?

G: What 'G' is a beetle whose larvae and females are luminous?

N: What 'N' is the varnish that men don't normally use?

C _____ B _____

I _____ Q _____

N _____ H _____

O _____ L _____

F _____ S _____

K _____ R _____

A _____ E _____

P _____ M _____

D _____ T _____

J _____ U _____

52

C: What 'C' was the first name of the judge called Humphreys, who was a leading Buddhist?

I: What 'I' is the ink or pencil or impression that cannot be blotted out or removed?

N: What 'N' was born at Burnham Thorpe in Norfolk and became an Admiral?

O: What 'O' is the opposite of under?

F: What 'F' goes with duddy to mean old fogey?

K: What 'K' is the great Russian chess player called Anatoly?

A: What 'A' is president of the 'Save the Children Fund' and is a princess?

P: What 'P' is weighted fishing tackle with hooks at intervals or is the supreme Christian prayer?

D: What 'D' is the castle used by Lord Wardens of the cinque ports?

J: What 'J' is to deride or scoff at?

B: What 'B' was the nickname of the Regency leader of fashion, called Mr Brummell?

Q: What 'Q' is the theory of physics associated with Max Planck?

H: What 'H' is the product that is hoped for by an Apiarist?

L: What 'L' is a German beer whose name means 'store' or 'keeping'?

S: What 'S' goes before loaf, beet and tongs?

R: What 'R' was spoilt and gave rise to the battle between Tweedledum and Tweedledee?

E: What 'E' is Jane Austen's eponymous heroine who married Mr Knightley?

M: What 'M' is President of Egypt?

T: What 'T' is a jacaranda?

U: What 'U' is to make a mark under a word, or syllable, to show it is to be emphasised?

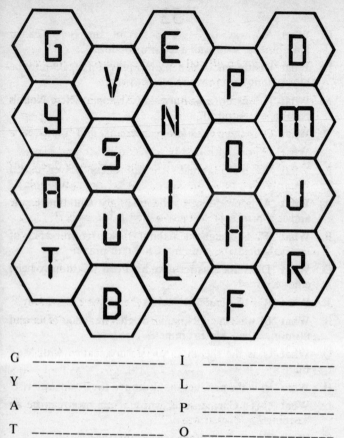

G _____ I _____

Y _____ L _____

A _____ P _____

T _____ O _____

V _____ H _____

S _____ F _____

U _____ D _____

B _____ M _____

E _____ J _____

N _____ R _____

53

G: What 'G' is the official robe of a university graduate?

Y: What 'Y' is the Abominable Snowman?

A: What 'A' are the mountains in Armenia where Noah's Ark came to rest?

T: What 'T' is a red fruit eaten in salads, and treated as a vegetable?

V: What 'V' is what the wind does when it changes direction?

S: What 'S' can be satin, chain, blanket or button-hole?

U: What 'U' is the muse of astronomy and the female equivalent of a planet discovered by Herschel?

B: What 'B' was the colour of the shirts worn by members of the Nazi party?

E: What 'E' comes after sure, to mean 'as might have been expected'?

N: What 'N' in Galilee was the home of the holy family?

I: What 'I' is a place to live, constructed of blocks of ice and snow?

L: What 'L' made Jonathan Swift's 'Journal to Stella'?

P: What 'P' can mean a portion of history, a full stop, or a complete sentence?

O: What 'O' is a heavy article of clothing that can be an 'ulster' or a 'British warm'?

H: What 'H' carries a lifeguard or pulls the cart?

F: What 'F' is the thighbone?

D: What 'D' do you fancy rather too often if you are a toper?

M: What 'M' is the Japanese Gilbert and Sullivan opera?

J: What 'J' was undoubtedly the most famous doctor born in Lichfield?

R: What 'R' was Johnny, an early punk?

C _____
E _____
I _____
N _____
R _____
W _____
D _____
K _____
B _____
V _____

F _____
T _____
S _____
Y _____
L _____
G _____
P _____
U _____
J _____
A _____

54

C: What 'C' in billiards is the substance you put on the end of your cue?

E: What 'E' do you keep on people that you watch?

I: What 'I' is a very black ink?

N: What 'N' were county cricket champions in 1981?

R: What 'R' is a hard biscuit eaten by a baby when teething?

W: What 'W' goes before ear, meal and germ?

D: What 'D' was called Walt and created Donald Duck?

K: What 'K' is Mr Dodd's adjective for the place called Ash?

B: What 'B' is a famous brewing town and was a famous actor?

V: What 'V' do you find in leaves, in rocks, or carrying blood to the heart?

F: What 'F' is the tree that produces cones?

T: What 'T' was once capital of Spain, and famous for sword steel?

S: What 'S' goes with beer, to symbolise 'an easy time'?

Y: What 'Y' in 'Boys from the Black Stuff' was the determined jobhunter?

L: What 'L' is galena, the commonest ore?

G: What 'G' is eaten by granivorous animals?

P: What 'P' means failure in an exam, pulling out feathers or bravery?

U: What 'U' were Cinderella's sisters?

J: What 'J' is the town in Andalusia that has given its name indirectly to sherry?

A: What 'A' was a famous saint of Padua, and a British Foreign Minister called Eden?

F _____   N _____

O _____   J _____

K _____   S _____

R _____   H _____

T _____   U _____

A _____   G _____

E _____   M _____

B _____   W _____

P _____   C _____

D _____   L _____

55

F: What 'F' is a conclusion arrived at before hearing any evidence?

O: What 'O' has a reputation for wisdom and flies and hunts by night?

K: What 'K' is a playing card showing a soldier or a servant?

R: What 'R' was the British scientist who first split the atom?

T: What 'T' has a new virtuoso called Wynton Marsalis?

A: What 'A' is a word from the Greek, meaning a denunciation or a curse?

E: What 'E' was the exclamation of Archimedes in his bath?

B: What 'B' is the canine symbol of Britain?

P: What 'P' is the white, hard, tasteless wax used to make candles?

D: What 'D' is a badger dog in Germany?

N: What 'N' goes before truth, ladies and ape?

J: What 'J' was a person of great patience in the Bible?

S: What 'S' is a holy place or a protected place where birds live in peace?

H: What 'H' was the deerstalker worn by Sherlock Holmes?

U: What 'U' is disarmament by only one side?

G: What 'G' is the name given to a fumbled attempt at a reef knot?

M: What 'M' was the car in which Alain Prost won the Grand Prix at Nurburgring?

W: What 'W' is a word used for a North American Indian dwelling?

C: What 'C' is the opuntia or prickly pear?

L: What 'L' is, basically, the offence committed by a burglar?

Solution: Puzzle 1

M: Moth; O: Oast; K: Kimberley; D: Dashes; J: John; P: Petition;
H: Helen; W: Water; F: Flower; B: Beer; L: Landslide; S: Solomon;
T: Tape; R: Riviera; C: Crimea; E: Epiphany; A: Addled; V: Vitamins;
G: Gag; N: Ney.

Solution: Puzzle 2

C: Chips; I: Impale; N: Nepal; O: Oboe; F: Floor; K: Kimono;
A: Abdicated; P: Peanuts; D: Duty; J: Jews; B: Beef; Q: Quart;
H: Harakiri; L: List; S: Stomach; R: Rearlight; E: Eskimos; M: Minestrone;
T: Tsetse; U: Umlaut.

Solution: Puzzle 3

G: Galahad; Y: Yoga; A: Ants; T: Torch; V: Vermin; S: Steam; U: Udder;
B: Bedouins; E: Excalibur; N: Nought; I: Immemorial; L: Leopard;
P: Planters; O: Outbreak; H: Hour; F: Feathers; D: Double; M: Marathon;
J: Jab; R: Raw.

Solution: Puzzle 4

C: Coventry; E: Ends; I: Impressionism; N: Normandy; R: Rabbit;
W: Water; D: Doodle; K: Kangchenjunga; B: Blue; V: Voluntary;
F: Fence; T: Triple; S: Starting; Y: Yam; L: Leveret; G: Gauntlet;
P: Perch; U: Umbria; J: Jersey; A: Apostles.

Solution: Puzzle 5

F: Flint; O: Outsider; K: Kruger; R: Rafter; T: Tuna (Tunny);
A: Adventure; E: Encore; B: Black; P: Poulterer; D: Dark; N: Nucleic
(Acid); J: Jacobean; S: Sage; H: Hares; U: Ur; G: Galaxy; M: Meridian;
W: Whisky; C: Catherine (The Great); L: Lava.

Solution: Puzzle 6

M: May; O: Oran; K: Kitty; D: Doyle; J: Joystick; P: Penguin;
H: Hydrant; W: Whale; F: Finger; B: Basques; L: Limericks; S: Somerset;
T: Tuxedo; R: Rhyming; C: Civilian; E: Edgar; A: Avon; V: Volcano (in
Mexico); G: Garret; N: Navigate.

Solution: Puzzle 7

C: Cloves; I: Ivory; N: Nine; O: Obey; F: Florida; K: King; A: Air;
P: Peasants; D: Durbar; J: Jot; B: Benny; Q: Quay; H: Hansard; L: Lime;
S: Step; R: Raisin; E: Erg; M: Mitre; T: Tutu; U: Unicorn.

Solution: Puzzle 8

G: Gibbet; Y: Yonghy; A: Alloy; T: Tom; V: Vat; S: Stone; U: Undertaker;
B: Beam; E: Exile; N: Nigeria; I: Ionic; L: Labyrinth; P: Plantagenets;
O: Over; H: Hull; F: Flax; D: Danger; M: Martha; J: Jack; R: Reaction.

Solution: Puzzle 9

C: Comets; E: Erin; I: Incognito; N: Nehru; R: Rand; W: Wasp;
D: Druids; K: Knots; B: Boxing; V: Volga; F: Fence; T: Trevino;
S: Saigon; Y: Yardarm; L: Life; G: Ginger; P: Perfumer; U: Ugli;
J: Jezebel; A: Ark.

Solution: Puzzle 10

F: Femur; O: Out; K: Klondyke; R: Rhone; T: Turkey; A: Advanced;
E: Evening; B: Boater; P: Potato; D: Day; N: Nugget; J: Jemmy; S: Stool;
H: Hung; U: Urban; G: Gunpowder; M: Moonwalking; W: Wonderland;
C: Centrifugal; L: Laugharne,

Solution: Puzzle 11

M: Merlin; O: Oatmeal; K: Kipling; D: Dame; J: Jack; P: Peacocks;
H: Hock; W: Wheel; F: Frogs; B: Bay; L: Lot; S: Stuart; T: Tiff;
R: Ride; C: Carpenter; E: Eskimos; A: Agenda; V: Violins; G: Genesis;
N: Nightingale.

Solution: Puzzle 12

C: Chicanes; I: Incinerator; N: Nixon; O: Ochre; F: Foreground; K: King;
A: Alcoholic; P: Pike; D: Dry; J: Jetlag; B: Belvoir (pron. Beever);
Q: Quail; H: Haemoglobin; L: Libretto; S: Sharp; R: Rhythm;
E: Eucalyptus; M: Minotaur; T: Tokyo; U: Usual.

Solution: Puzzle 13

G: Gainsborough; Y: Ye; A: Altar; T: Tarpaulin; V: Vim; S: Shock; U: Ukraine; B: Belgium; E: Exchequer; N: Nose; I: Indianapolis; L: Levi; P: Patchwork (Quilt); O: Overbooking; H: Hay; F: Fingers; D: Denver; M: Mohammed; J: Jack; R: Ruby.

Solution: Puzzle 14

C: Coo; E: Ethnic; I: Incandescent; N: Newton; R: Raid; W: Wise; D: Destroyers; K: Kelvin; B: Buxton; V: Vow; F: Fenians; T: Tie; S: Sauna; Y: Yank; L: Liffey; G: Guru; P: Port; U: Untouchables; J: Jiff or jiffy; A: Artichoke.

Solution: Puzzle 15

F: Flute; O: Ounce; K: Kent; R: Raspberry; T: Torpedo; A: Antifreeze; E: Eve; B: Bingo; P: Piccalilli; D: Dam; N: Nosegay; J: Jack; S: Supremes; H: Horseradish; U: Ukraine; G: Glencoe; M: Major; W: Water; C: (Prince) Charles; L: Leech.

Solution: Puzzle 16

M: Marsh; O: Oar; K: Kneecap; D: Duce; J: Jackdaw; P: Poppy; H: Holbein; W: Weak; F: Fourth; B: Bush; L: Leather; S: Sedan; T: Tudor; R: Ribs; C: Calcutta; E: Easter; A: Androcles; V: Vol au vent; G: Gruel; N: Noele.

Solution: Puzzle 17

C: Chimpanzee; I: Israel; N: Nickel; O: Off (white); F: Front; K: Kentucky; A: Act; P: Pampas; D: Dublin; J: Java; B: Barley; Q: Qualms; H: Hunchback; L: Lyrics; S: Shinto; R: Railway; E: Ewing; M: Missionary; T: Tartan; U: Uniform.

Solution: Puzzle 18

G: Gullet; Y: Yemen; A: Anorexia; T: Tributary; V: Volley; S: Snake; U: Ulna; B: Beirut; E: Excavation; N: Nephew; I: Implode; L: Leading (Aircraftsman): P: 'Punchlines'; O: Outbid; H: Hebrides; F: Foxhole; D: Disraeli; M: Mafeking; J: Jane; R: Rear.

Solution: Puzzle 19

C: Consolation; E: Etiquette; I: Indians; N: Ned; R: Rabbit (punch); W: Wager; D: Dekker; K: Kennedy; B: Belinda; V: Visa; F: Flood; T: Tin; S: Sagittarius; Y: Yak; L: Lapis lazuli; G: Gestapo; P: Port; U: Unisex; J: John; A: Apple.

Solution: Puzzle 20

F: Flap; O: Ossified; K: Kale (or kail); R: Roe; T: Trawler; A: Amethyst; E: Ell; B: Butterflies; P: Pi; D: Dances; N: Numerator; J: Jute; S: Squint; H: Harpsichord; U: Uvula; G: Greenwich; M: Maria; W: Wind; C: Church; L: Libya.

Solution: Puzzle 21

M: Mayday; O: Obey; K: Kickstarter; D: Dead; J: Jury; P: Paw; H: Hook; W: Window; F: Fox; B: Badminton; L: Leather; S: Subtitles; T: Transpose; R: Risorgimento; C: Chieftain; E: Eau de Cologne; A: Amazon; V: Vanity; G: Grave; N: Norway.

Solution: Puzzle 22

C: Callan; I: Ionosphere; N: Night; O: Objector; F: Frizzy; K: Khaki; A: Alimony; P: Passenger; D: Diaghilev; J: Jardinière; B: Banbury; Q: Quitter; H: Homeopathy; L: Latimer; S: Spring; R: Rally; E: Eyelets; M: Methylated; T: Toupee; U: Utrillo.

Solution: Puzzle 23

G: Gangway; Y: Yosemite (pron. Yohsemity); A: Anne; T: Tent; V: Vulture; S: Spanish; U: Ulysses; B: Birthday; E: Ermine; N: Nitrogen; I: Indian; L: Larboard; P: 'Pygmalion'; O: Out; H: Hyde; F: Fred; D: Donkey; M: Mafia; J: Jesus; R: Rastas/Rastafarianism.

Solution: Puzzle 24

C: Colonel; E: Euclid; I: Ignatius; N: Nock; R: Race (meeting); W: Wealthy; D: Deuce; K: Kerosene; B: Brodie (Miss Jean); V: Velvet; F: Ferraro; T: Tucker (Jenkins); S: Scaffold; Y: Yew; L: Labyrinth; G: Geyser; P: Prospect; U: Ursa Major; J: Joint; A: Achates.

Solution: Puzzle 25

F: Flattery; O: Over; K: Kissing; R: Rummage; T: Truant; A: Absent-minded; E: Elk; B: Buttons; P: Piggyback or Pick-a-back; D: Dumas; N: Née; J: Jester; S: Salisbury; H: Huguenots; U: Ugly; G: Gris-Nez; M: Mitch; W: Whisky; C: Chamberlain; L: Lima.

Solution: Puzzle 26

M: Matt; O: Oberon; K: Krypton; D: Dentifrice; J: Jenny; P: Petty; H: Holland; W: Warren; F: Faust; B: Brace; L: Liberals; S: Stable; T: Tummy; R: Rind; C: Coxswain; E: Eagle; A: Air; V: Vanessa (well-known 30s painter); G: Grin; N: Norfolk.

Solution: Puzzle 27

C: Clerk; I: Incisors; N: Net; O: Occupy; F: Fronds; K: Keating; A: Alley; P: Paragon; D: Dutch; J: Jack; B: Baltic; Q: Quavery; H: Herd; L: Loom; S: Sand; R: Ramble; E: Explosives; M: Mercury; T: Tent; U: Udder.

Solution: Puzzle 28

G: Germany; Y: Yugoslavia; A: Amputation; T: Toads; V: Ventricles; S: Spirit; U: Ultravox; B: Beaverbrook; E: Ernie; N: Nuns; I: Ian; L: Limpet; P: Palatine; O: Ounce; H: Harold; F: Fortran; D: Dolmen; M: Mumps; J: Jericho; R: Red.

Solution: Puzzle 29

C: Christopher; E: Ethyl; I: Identity; N: Newlaid; R: Reversing; W: Water; D: Depression; K: Kingcup; B: Bowie; V: Vermeer; F: Freeze; T: Terrier; S: Solitaire; Y: Yeast; L: Leamington; G: Goose (flesh); P: Prussia; U: Uruguay; J: Josephine; A: Accumulator.

Solution: Puzzle 30

F: Flautist; O: Orion; K: Knots; R: Romanoff; T: Tudors (Henry VII and VIII, Mary, Edward VI and Elizabeth); A: Absentee; E: Embalm; B: Best; P: Perez; D: Delhi; N: National; J: Jam; S: Scorpio or Scorpion; H: Hive; U: Uncle; G: Golding; M: Marilyn; W: Waist; C: Chihuahua; L: Lion.

Solution: Puzzle 31

M: Magnesium; O: Oboe; K: Kit; D: Dry; J: Jetsam; P: Palmistry; H: Horse; W: Walesa (Lech); F: Fiesta; B: Black; L: Lucre; S: Sandy; T: Tomato; R: Rain; C: Chorister; E: Emmy; A: Apes (Note: don't accept 'animals'); V: Virginia; G: Graphite; N: Nazareth.

Solution: Puzzle 32

C: Crevasse; I: Idomeneo; N: Norman; O: Octavo; F: Front; K: Kent; A: Almshouse; P: Parsley; D: Dyke; J: Jehovah; B: Becket; Q: Queen; H: Hitler; L: Lungs; S: Sea; R: Ramparts; E: Eye; M: Marquee; T: Tiddlywinks; U: Utopia.

Solution: Puzzle 33

G: Glastonbury; Y: Yester; A: America; T: Type; V: Velocity; S: Skin; U: Uncut; B: 'Bullseye'; E: Entire; N: Nixon; I: Ignorance; L: Lifeboat; P: Pakistan; O: Odyssey; H: Higgins; F: Fortyniners; D: Deadly; M: Mercator; J: Jar; R; Reaper.

Solution: Puzzle 34

C: Chaplin; E: Enoch; I: Iraq; N: Ninety; R: Rake; W: Willow (pattern); D: Darning; K: Kidney; B: Bare; V: Veteran; F: Frogmen; T: Torah; S: Scarecrow; Y: Yankee; L: Lebanon; G: Gene; P: Premature; U: Upstream (or Upriver); J: Jolson (Al); A: Ajar.

Solution: Puzzle 35

F: Floor; O: Oxen; K: Khan; R: Rockall; T: Tunnel (first under-water tunnel in the world, now used by the tube); A: Abridge; E: Eire; B: Bunk; P: Perseus; D: Darnley; N: Newman; J: Jawbone; S: Stowaway; H: Hubble; U: Utopia; G: Gnash; M: Marconi; W: Wedge; C: Cabbage; L: Leaf.

Solution: Puzzle 36

M: Midnight; O: Opal; K: Kremlin; D: Doublet; J: Jabberwocky; P: Paradise; H: Hamlet; W: Wilkie; F: Flint; B: Box; L: Lilies; S: Samson; T: Tommy; R: Rubbish; C: Chestnuts; E: Emmerdale; A: Arbroath (Note: a form of small smoked haddock); V: Vostok; G: Greyhound; N: Netherlands.

Solution: Puzzle 37

C: Croak; I: Iolanthe; N: Nazi; O: Overcast; F: Frequent; K: Krugerrand; A: Amicable; P: Pioneer; D: Dracula; J: Jekyll; B: Balls; Q: Quills; H: Hamburg; L: Leprosy; S: Snap; R: Rugged; E: Epsom; M: Manifesto; T: Thursday; U: Usurper.

Solution: Puzzle 38

G: Gnome; Y: Yokohama; A: Angelus; T: Tom; V: Vulpine; S: Story; U: Upsidedown; B: (The) Beatles; E: Entertainment; N: Nicaragua; I: India; L: Lettuce; P: Periodical; O: Oxford; H: Howdah; F: Fox; D: Dominoes; M: Mary; J: Jam; R: Raincoat.

Solution: Puzzle 39

C: Chlorine; E: Exeter; I: Inkling; N: Noel; R: Ringmaster; W: Warder; D: Dollar; K: Krushchev; B: Bunker; V: Vivid; F: Flags; T: Tot; S: Salad; Y: Yaw; L: Leek; G: Greater; P: Physician; U: Undergraduate; J: Jute; A: Acute.

Solution: Puzzle 40

F: Fox; O: Opal; K: Kissing; R: Robinson; T: Tumulus (Tump); A: Abolitionist; E: Ejector; B: Bashful; P: Pitch; D: Dame; N: Needles; J: Joe; S: Star; H: Halides; U: Umbrella; G: Great; M: Maiden; W: Warhead; C: Cavalry; L: Larynx.

Solution: Puzzle 41

M: Martyr; O: Overdraft; K: Kingfisher; D: Denmark; J: Just; P: Pentateuch; H: Hamlet; W: Windsor; F: Fruit; B: Bodleian; L: Lockjaw; S: Sage; T: Trot; R: Rebecca; C: Coronary; E: Ethel; A: Albatross; V: Viper; G: Grouse; N: Nepal.

Solution: Puzzle 42

C: Crockett; I: Investor; N: Nineteen; O: Oval; F: Friendly; K: Kettle; A: Acre; P: Placate; D: Drums; J: Jane; B: Bakewell; Q: Quarrel; H: Homer; L: Log; S: Stirrup; R: Rajah; E: Elm; M: Morocco; T: Timbuktu; U: Underarm.

Solution: Puzzle 43

G: Gladstone; Y: Yo-yo; A: Ambridge; T: Terry; V: Vulcanise; S: Sun;
U: (Peter) Ustinov; B: Bird; E: Every; N: Niagara; I: 'Imagine'; L: Letters;
P: Permafrost; O: Ovett; H: Hydrogen; F: Foundling; D: Doyley;
M: Moscow; J: Jiggery; R: Reed.

Solution: Puzzle 44

C: Chip; E: Ergo; I: Inch; N: Natasha; R: Rosary; W: Wally; D: Dante;
K: Knot; B: Barry; V: Vole; F: Flakes; T: Telford; S: Stern; Y: Yokel;
L: Luddites; G: Granulated; P: Piecemeal; U: Ultimatum; J: January;
A: Angel.

Solution: Puzzle 45

F: Floppy; O: Osprey; K: Klaxon; R: Rome; T: Tziganes; A: Alsatian;
E: Evening; B: Browning; P: Penguin; D: Damsel; N: Nape; J: Jackie;
S: Scotland; H: Hardy; U: Ursula; G: Grizzly; M: Marseillaise; W: Weepie;
C: Curtain; L: Lochs.

Solution: Puzzle 46

M: Motel; O: Oratorio; K: Knife; D: Dogstar; J: John; P: Party;
H: Hoover; W: Waders, F. Flee, B: Bean; L: Locomotives; S: Senate;
T: Toll; R: Roy; C: Chef d'Oeuvre; E: Evaporated; A: Angle; V: Viscount;
G: Garbage; N: New.

Solution: Puzzle 47

C: Chuck; I: Insecticides; N: No; O: Ouse; F: Foretell; K: Kawasaki;
A: Anagram; P: Pearly; D: Downing; J: Jelly; B: Bairn; Q: Quaver;
H: 'Hallelujah'; L: Lent; S: Spring; R: Ramshackle; E: Emetic;
M: Moccasin; T: Thaw; U: Understand.

Solution: Puzzle 48

G: Guy; Y: Yoke; A: Andrew; T: Trafalgar; V: Vowel; S: Station;
U: Upshot; B: British; E: Everest; N: Nippers; I: Imitation; L: Liberty;
P: Perishable; O: O'Brien; H: Halley; F: Foursome; D: Doolittle;
M: Mullet; J: Jig; R: Roundabout.

Solution: Puzzle 49

C: Chad; E: Esquire; I: Independent; N: Nobbled; R: Rough; W: White-chapel; D: Dairy; K: Kublai Khan; B: Bodie; V: Vulgate; F: Fish; T: Temple (Note: so called because it once belonged to the Knights Templar whose round church still survives there); S: Sorbonne; Y: Yodel; L: Laureate; G: Grease; P: Philippines; U: Usher (Note: official in Parliament representing the Queen); J: Jutland; A: Ace.

Solution: Puzzle 50

F: Forget; O: Orchestra; K: Knee; R: Rota; T: Truman; A: Ali Baba; E: Elixir; B: Blackpool; P: Pericles; D: Date; N: Noddy; J: Jaundice; S: Sinister; H: Head; U: Upper; G: Greece; M: Matinée; W: Washing; C: Commercials; L: Loft.

Solution: Puzzle 51

M: Mazurka; O: Overtime; K: Kilt; D: Dough; J: Juke (box); P: Plimsoll; H: Hallmark; W: Wizard; F: Friends; B: Barrie (J. M.); L: Loiter(ing); S: Silo; T: Trust; R: Rick; C: Cavaliers; E: Expire; A: Africa; V: Valediction; G: Glow-worm; N: Nail.

Solution: Puzzle 52

C: Christmas; I: Indelible; N: Nelson; O: Over; F: Fuddy; K: Karpov; A: Anne; P: Paternoster; D: Dover; J: Jeer; B: Beau; Q: Quantum; H: Honey; L: Lager; S: Sugar; R: Rattle; E: Emma; M: Mubaraq; T: Tree (with scented wood and blue flowers); U: Underline.

Solution: Puzzle 53

G: Gown; Y: Yeti; A: Ararat; T: Tomato; V: Veers; S: Stitch; U: Urania (planet is Uranus); B: Brown; E: Enough; N: Nazareth; I: Igloo; L: Letters; P: Period; O: Overcoat; H: Horse; F: Femur; D: Drink; M: 'Mikado'; J: Johnson; R: Rotten.

Solution: Puzzle 54

C: Chalk; E: Eye; I: Indian; N: Nottingham; R: Rusk; W: Wheat; D: Disney; K: Knotty; B: Burton; V: Veins; F: Fir; T: Toledo; S: Skittle(s); Y: Yosser; L: Lead; G: Grass; P: Pluck; U: Ugly; J: Jerez; A: Anthony.

Solution: Puzzle 55

F: Foregone; O: Owl; K: Knave; R: Rutherford; T: Trumpet; A: Anathema;
E: Eureka!; B: Bulldog; P: Paraffin; D: Dachshund; N: Naked; J: Job;
S: Sanctuary; H: Hat; Unilateral; G: Granny; M: Maclaren; W: Wigwam;
C: Cactus; L: Larceny.

A SELECTION OF BESTSELLERS
FROM SPHERE

FICTION

FOOTFALL	Niven & Pournelle	£3.95 ☐
PRIVATE AFFAIRS	Judith Michael	£4.95 ☐
STREET SONG	Emma Blair	£3.50 ☐
GOLDEN TRIPLE TIME	Zoe Garrison	£2.95 ☐
BEACHES	Iris Rainer Dart	£2.95 ☐

FILM & TV TIE-IN

MONA LISA	John Luther Novak	£2.50 ☐
BLOCKBUSTERS GOLD RUN		£1.95 ☐
9½ WEEKS	Elizabeth McNeil	£1.95 ☐
BOON	Anthony Masters	£2.50 ☐
AUF WIEDERSEHEN PET 2	Fred Taylor	£2.75 ☐

NON-FICTION

MY MOTHER'S KEEPER	B. D. Hyman	£3.50 ☐
BURTON: THE MAN BEHIND THE MYTH	Penny Junor	£2.95 ☐
THE DISAPPEARED	John Simpson & Jana Bennett	£4.95 ☐
THE LAST NAZI: THE LIFE AND TIMES OF JOSEPH MENGELE	Gerald Astor	£3.50 ☐
THE FALL OF SAIGON	David Butler	£3.95 ☐

All Sphere books are available at your local bookshop or newsagent, or can be ordered direct from the publisher. Just tick the titles you want and fill in the form below.

Name _____

Address _____

_____

Write to Sphere Books, Cash Sales Department, P.O. Box 11, Falmouth, Cornwall TR10 9EN.

Please enclose a cheque or postal order to the value of the cover price plus:

UK: 55p for the first book, 22p for the second book and 14p for each additional book ordered to a maximum charge of £1.75.

OVERSEAS: £1.00 for the first book plus 25p per copy for each additional book.

BFPO & EIRE: 55p for the first book, 22p for the second book plus 14p per copy for the next 7 books, thereafter 8p per book.

Sphere Books reserve the right to show new retail prices on covers which may differ from those previously advertised in the text or elsewhere, and to increase postal rates in accordance with the PO.